Markham & Co. of Chesterfield 1889–1998

An Illustrated History

K.G. Wort
and M.G. Bennett

MERTON

First published 2005

Published by
Merton Priory Press Ltd
67 Merthyr Road, Whitchurch
Cardiff CF14 1DD

© K.G. Wort and M.G. Bennett 2005

ISBN 1 898937 64 8

Printed by
Dinefwr Press Ltd
Rawlings Road, Llandybie
Carmarthenshire SA18 3YD

Contents

Products and markets, *continued*

List of Illustrations

Acknowledgements

We are indebted to Prof. S.D. Chapman, formerly of the University of Nottingham, who wrote an excellent account of the Staveley Company in his book *Stanton and Staveley* (Woodhead-Faulkner, 1981), from which we have reproduced a number of illustrations and references with his kind permission. We are also indebted to Staveley Industries plc.

We have been assisted by employees of Markham and must mention Malcolm Lindley, Gordon Scott and John Whysall who read the draft script and added useful comments, for which many thanks. Margaret Butler and Chris Bird diligently proof read the text.

Note on sources

Apart from Prof. Chapman's book, this study is based almost entirely on records and photographs in the authors' possession collected during their long period of service, much of it at board level, with Markham, and on their own memories of the company over the last forty years. For this reason detailed references have not been given. Readers who would like to follow up particular points are welcome to write to the authors at the publisher's address.

1 Charles Paxton Markham (1865–1926), from a painting by Richard Jack (1866–1952).

Introduction

The history of Markham & Co. Ltd is a story of engineering achievements and disappointments covering one hundred and ten years of trading activities from 1888 to 1998, when Markham's works were closed.

In preparing a study of the affairs of the company whilst on the Broad Oaks site, it is easy to lose sight of the external local, national and international environment and events, which conditioned the way in which a general engineering company had to operate. Two World Wars, economic slumps and booms, devaluation, nationalisations and privatisations, exchange controls and inflation all posed their particular problems, and sometimes opportunities, to a small heavy engineering company building custom-made plant with delivery periods sometimes as long as five years.

Political, economic and technical changes altered the life and prospects of both products and customers. The British coal industry was, for most of the lifetime of Markham, a pillar of the order book and this had all but disappeared by the 1990s.

The development of large capacity hydraulic mobile cranes introduced low-cost competition for heavy fabrications. Computer-controlled machining and fabrication deskilled many operations which were previously the province of skilled craftsmen. Much of this work has migrated to the Far East and to Eastern Europe where labour costs are low yet computer literacy is high and where a willingness to invest in capital plant has generated a very competitive manufacturing environment.

Apart from the C.P. Markham years between 1889 and 1924, Markham was a relatively small component of a larger group. The Staveley Coal & Iron Company, owners from 1924 to 1937, was a large coalmining, ironmaking and chemical concern. John Brown (1937–86), after the nationalisation of their steelworks, was in the words of the *Economist*, 'a rag bag of engineering companies'. Trafalgar House (1986–96), was a conglomerate originating as property developers who then moved into engineering with the acquisition of Cleveland Bridge, Cementation and John Brown. Kvaerner (1996–8) is a Norwegian engineering group who purchased Trafalgar House.

Kvaerner integrated Markham with their Davy, Sheffield, engineering group, which resulted in the closure of Broad Oaks works in Chesterfield. Kvaerner sold the land to a property developer who has since built a large housing estate on the site. This was the final sorry chapter in the history of Markham & Company.

Our business history begins in the 1830s with Oliver's works in Chesterfield. This is followed by C.P. Markham's purchase of Oliver's Broad Oaks works in 1889 and then John Brown's period of ownership. The main biographical narrative begins in 1958. From this date forward one or other of the two authors was employed by Markham & Co. up until 1993. Thus the last forty years of the company's existence can be told from personal experience and, with a number of other employees still living, the narrative is augmented by their reminiscences.

We have divided the history into three distinct sections. The first section tells the story in terms of the owners' influence, and that of significant external events, while the second relates to what Markham did and the type of products they made. Appendices 1 to 3 list details of the three principal products. Finally, the third section describes the daily routine, the social activities and some of the company's characters.

The company's first fifty years of existence was intimately bound up with the Staveley Coal & Iron Company, with C.P. Markham in charge of both Staveley and Markham & Co. from 1889 to 1924. After his death Markham & Co. was owned by Staveley until 1936, and so it was inevitable that Markham should produce a great deal of the plant required to equip Staveley's expanding iron and chemical works.

Unfortunately many of the early records of Markham's business affairs, up until about the 1950s, have been lost or destroyed in the various changes of ownership and closure. Thus it has not been possible to present any financial data in this early period.

To cope with variations in trade and technology the Broad Oaks Works changed its shape and nature over its life. The iron, brass and white metal foundries and the forge were closed as more competitive specialist suppliers emerged. The erecting (assembly) shops were extended to handle larger components, and heavier cranes were installed. This was largely to cater for increases in the physical size of water turbine and tunnelling machinery. Design and manufacturing standards became more stringent, both nationally and internationally, and compliance with quality assurance and Health and Safety procedures was instituted.

In the early days the company was run by engineering entrepreneurs designing in-house most of the output, much of which was in repetitive yet custom built product lines. Latterly, in-house design, apart from mine winders and tunnel boring machines, only accounted for a small portion of Markham's turnover. Reliance was placed on water turbines and other subcontract work with virtually no dependence on repetitive product lines. In addition, the owners, after the Second World War, failed to invest sufficiently in plant modernisation, succumbing to the 'British disease'. Machines obtained as war reparations were still being used until the demise of the works. Attempts were made to acquire repetitive product lines by both in-house and external design with products such as pneumatic stowing and conveying, die-casting

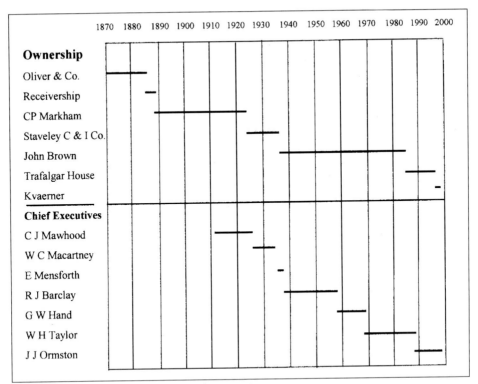

2 Historical outline of ownership and management.

machines, paper converting machines and wind turbines. However the demise of the coal industry, the rise of low-cost Eastern European and Asian manufacture and an inability by UK companies to penetrate the wind turbine market put paid to these aspirations.

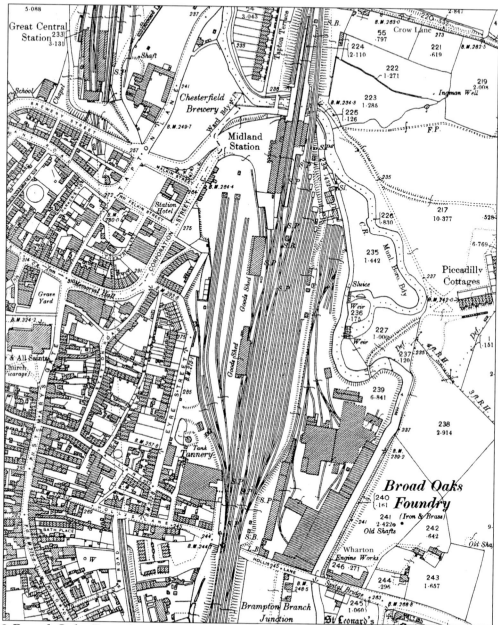

3 Broad Oaks Foundry, *c.*1900, from the 1:2500 Ordnance Survey map.

Historical Overview

A synopsis of the history of Markham & Co. Ltd

Engineering manufacture commenced on the Broad Oaks site in 1872 following the purchase of about 25 acres of land by William Oliver two years earlier so that he could relocate his Victoria Foundry works from Knifesmithgate in central Chesterfield to a larger area at Spital on the eastern edge of the town.

Between 1872 and 1998, when manufacture ended at Broad Oaks, the works had six owners. Oliver's tenure of the site lasted from 1870 to 1886, when Oliver & Co. went into liquidation. Charles Paxton Markham, a director of Staveley Coal & Iron Co., bought the works from the receiver in 1889, and established Markham & Co Ltd. Markham became chairman of Staveley Coal & Iron Co. in 1903 and both Markham and Staveley flourished under his leadership. Markham sold Markham & Co. to Staveley Coal & Iron Co. in 1924 and Markham remained as a Staveley subsidiary company until it was purchased by John Brown & Co. in 1937. Markham passed into the Trafalgar House group when John Brown was taken over in 1986. In 1996 Trafalgar House was taken over by the Norwegian Kvaerner group and Markham was incorporated into the power section of the group.

Shortly after the takeover Markham was transferred in 1998 to the metals division of the Kvaerner group and integrated with Davy Metals in Sheffield. This involved the transfer to Sheffield of the Markham design office team and a small number of works, sales and accounts personnel, together with a number of the larger machine tools. The Chesterfield works were closed and put up for sale.

1830–86: The Olivers, engineering factory owners

John Oliver, who was a friend of George Stephenson, started business as a blacksmith in Blacksmith's Yard off Holywell Street in Chesterfield in the 1830s. William Oliver, John's son, joined the business, which was expanded to include coach building and wheelwright work, employing up to 40 men. In 1854 the business moved to Victoria Foundry off Knifesmithgate in the centre of Chesterfield and expanded to incorporate ironfounding, machine building, turning, pattern making and fitting.

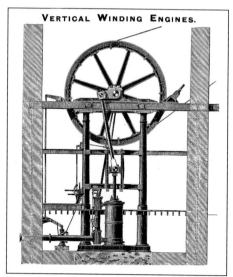

VERTICAL WINDING ENGINES.

4 A typical Oliver product.

John Oliver died in 1862. William Oliver developed the business to build small steam engines and produce architectural ironwork, for example for Chesterfield parish church, Clay Cross church and Arkwright Hall. He then started manufacturing mining machinery such as pit tub wheels, headgear pulleys and pumping engines. Customers included Tapton Coal & Iron works.

In 1865 Olivers, now employing 130 people, became a limited company with a capital of £8,640 and began building mine winding engines. The works then stretched from Knifesmithgate to Saltergate. In 1869 turning and fitting shops were added together with an erecting shop with a gantry crane. Boiler making and the repair of locomotives commenced. The first mine winder was delivered to Pleasley colliery. This was driven by a 26 in. diameter cylinder steam engine and had a single drum. A winder for a colliery at Clay Cross was delivered in 1870.

Also in 1870 some 5¼ acres of land were acquired at Broad Oaks, where in 1872 development began in readiness to build a factory. The river Rother was straightened to provide additional space and brick clay was excavated to provide material for works buildings. Plate 1 is a plan of Chesterfield and shows the location of the Broad Oaks works.

Oliver's moved to Broad Oaks in 1872–4 and between 1873 and 1878 winders were supplied to Holmewood, Pilsley, Grassmoor and Silverhill mines. In 1878–80 a boiler shop was built. Orders for 20 rock drills with air compressors were received from A. Schram as well as orders for railway wagons, bridge and crane girders, boilers, engines and pumps for iron and water works and blast furnaces for Holywell Iron works and for Bestwood Coal & Iron Company. In 1881–5 Olivers began building locomotives and hauling engines for coalmines as well as coal washing machinery and coal elevators. They built blast furnaces and blast stoves for the Wingerworth Iron Company and Skinningrove Ironworks. They also began to export: for example mine winders for Canada and girders to India and Australia. They were placed on the Admiralty list. By this time the works site had expanded to eight acres and the company employed 180 people.

In 1886 Olivers went into liquidation.

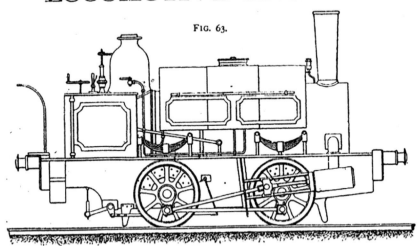

MINING MACHINERY AND APPLIANCES.

LOCOMOTIVE ENGINES.

FIG. 63.

Our Locomotives, FIG. 63, are specially adapted for colliery shunting and similar work where sharp curves and irregular roads have to be constantly run over.

The following description may be taken as an abridged specification.

The boiler barrel, smoke box, tube plate, dome, and fire box, are of Lowmoor, Bowling, or Taylor's best Yorkshire plate.

The inside fire box of the best selected copper, the screwed stays for the fire box of soft rolled copper.

And the tubes of solid drawn brass.

The frame plates are of Yorkshire or equal quality of iron, fitted with cast-iron axle box guides, the axle boxes are of cast-iron fitted with gun-metal steps.

The cylinders are made from best cold blast cast-iron as hard as can be bored, all joints being surfaced.

All working parts are of the best selected scrap or best cold blast cast-iron, all wrought iron working parts being case hardened. The slide bars are of steel, connecting and coupling rods of the best selected scrap, and fitted with gun-metal steps, axles of best selected scrap. Wheels of tough cast-iron, tyres of Bessemer steel. The springs of the best manufacture.

The boiler is tested to a pressure of 200 lbs. on the square inch with water, and to 150 lbs. with steam.

The workmanship and material are of the best of their respective kinds, and equal to such as is accepted by the principal English Railway Companies. The Engines are painted and supplied with all necessary tools ready for being put to work.

LOCOMOTIVES LET ON HIRE.

We keep Locomotives in stock for the purpose of letting them on hire to customers while their own Locomotives are being repaired.

OLIVER AND CO., Limited, Broad Oaks Iron Works, Chesterfield.

5 A page from an Oliver catalogue.

1889–1924: Charles Paxton Markham: founder and owner of Markham for 35 years

Charles Markham senior, the son of a Northamptonshire solicitor, was an engineer who became locomotive superintendent of the Midland Railway Company at Derby. He was responsible for pioneering work on locomotive firebox construction and in particular patented his invention of the firebrick arch over the fire bed, which greatly increased the efficiency of the coal combustion in the firebox. In 1860 Richard Barrow, who was then proprietor of Staveley Ironworks, persuaded Markham to move to Staveley as managing director and chief executive. In 1862 Markham married Rosa Paxton, daughter of Sir Joseph Paxton MP, the agent for the Duke of Devonshire and designer of the Crystal Palace exhibition hall. Markham became chairman of Staveley in 1865 was responsible for increasing cast iron production threefold. By 1870 Staveley was among the largest cast iron producers in Britain, if not the world. The company established its chemical business in 1873.

Charles Markham senior died in 1888, whereupon his son, Charles Paxton Markham, born at Brimington Hall in 1865, who had joined Staveley on

6 *Gladys*, an 0-4-0 shunting locomotive built by Markham in 1894, now preserved at the Midland Railwaty Centre, Butterley.

leaving school, was elected to the Staveley board of directors. On 21 June that year Messrs Oliver's Broad Oaks engineering works was offered for sale by auction. There was no bid! The following year C.P. Markham, aged 23, purchased the works, some eight acres in area, in order to specialise in the manufacture and installation of blast furnaces, rolling mills, locomotives and colliery equipment. The work in progress, which he inherited, included winders for Grassmoor and Alfreton collieries and eight tunnelling shields for J.W. Williams.

In 1891 Markham married Margaret 'Daisy' Jackson, daughter of the chairman of the rival Clay Cross Company. They had no children. It was a stormy marriage, he with his dark good looks and she being a remarkably handsome woman played the role of 'Lord and lady bountiful' with considerable style. They enjoyed their cruises in their private yacht in the Mediterranean and around Scandinavia and holidays on their grouse moor in Scotland. She encouraged CP to involve himself in local politics and he served three terms as mayor of Chesterfield and as chairman of the local bench. Although he had no appetite for national politics, he gave some desultory support to his brother Sir Arthur who was the Liberal MP for Mansfield from the turn of the century until 1916.

7 A 300 hp endless electrically driven colliery hauler.

In 1892 the Chesterfield boundary was extended, which brought Broad Oaks works within the borough. By 1900 Markham & Co. was employing 600 workers. In 1903 Markham became chairman of Staveley Iron & Coal Co. Ltd. He lived at Hasland Hall and later moved to Ringwood Hall near Brimington, which he left to the Staveley Company in 1926. He was never short of money, having inherited a sizeable fortune from his father. He enjoyed a flamboyant lifestyle, preferring to drive and be driven in a glorious primrose yellow Rolls Royce more than anything more mundane.

In 1910 the *Colliery Guardian* printed an 11-page article, incorporating eight full-page photographs, describing the Broad Oaks Ironworks of Markham & Co., summing up the wide range of machine tools and plant which was being fully utilised to manufacture a diverse range of products designed 'in house'. The site then occupied 25 acres with direct railway access to both the Midland Railway and the Great Central Railway. The chief products of the works consisted of colliery machinery of all descriptions, and structural ironwork, but a variety of other classes of machinery was also manufactured, including heavy castings, colliery locomotives and rock drills.

There was a single machine shop consisting of nine bays each with a 25 ton capacity travelling crane. One of the largest machines was a boring and turning mill able to handle a work piece 26 ft in diameter by 10 ft high. There was also a planing machine able to plane a workpiece, such as a cast iron mine winder steam engine bed, 10 ft wide by 30 ft long. The machine could

8 The German crane, for many years a landmark at Broad Oaks.

9 An advertisement for Markham's Ford motor car agency.

plane both crossways and lengthways without moving the workpiece. There were lathes able to machine shafts 30 ft in length by 3 ft in diameter and bore cylinders up to 110 in. in diameter. There was a continuous programme of replacement of older machines with the most modern equivalent. The company was contemplating installing a mill to take diameters up to 36 ft for turning winder drums.

There was a central tool and gauge room. 'This standardisation is insisted upon throughout the works, so that duplicate parts can be ordered without hesitancy, and with the knowledge in advance that the fit will be accurate.'

The erecting shop adjoining the machine shop was 50 ft wide, 340 ft long and 30 ft high to the crane track, and was served by three electric 30 ton capacity travelling cranes. There were also two large erecting pits, for building vertical engines or other machinery having great height. There was a steam main at 160 lb/sq. in. pressure as well as compressed air and water hydraulic power distributed throughout the shop. The shops were heated by live steam panels attached to each column.

Since most products were made of iron the foundry was the hub of the works. It had three bays, two of them 50 ft wide by 300 ft long which were being lengthened at the time by another 160 ft. One bay had a 45 ton capacity crane and two circular casting pits, 20 ft in diameter and 24 ft deep. The second bay had three 20 ton electric travelling cranes whilst the third bay was devoted to core making with six large drying ovens. The roofs of the shops could be lifted off by the 'German' stockyard crane.

There was a separate structural department with three bays each 45 ft wide by 400 ft long, each equipped with a 20 ton electric crane and a number of jib cranes. There was a large erecting pit and testing area for building tunnel driving shields for which the firm was well known, having supplied the largest shields in the world for the Rotherhithe tunnel. A template loft 40 ft wide by 160 ft long enabled full size complex marking out and drilling templates to be made. This was still in use in the early 1960s.

Iron production at Staveley doubled between 1900 and 1914 and joint ven-

10 Cylindro-conical colliery winder drums.

tures were established with John Brown and with the Bestwood Coal and Iron Company in order to exploit new iron ore quarries. Staveley built three new blast furnaces, with an associated coking plant. C.P. Markham acted as the engineer and by working virtually day and night completed the project in two years. The new ovens could process local soft coal and gave rise to the extension of the chemical works, where the sulphate, tar distillation, benzene and sulphuric acid plants made a valuable contribution to the company's activities. In addition, in 1914 Markham was importing Ford cars for sale and was the company's sole agent in the district.

In 1925 C.P. Markham married his cousin, Mrs Francis Marjory Nunneley. He died the following year aged 61, bequeathing his whole estate, valued at £600,000, to his wife, who in turn gave Ringwood Hall and estate to the Staveley Company to become a social centre and playground for the employees. At this time Staveley and its subsidiaries employed 37,000 people, their collieries produced 10 million tons of coal a year and their ironstone mines produced a million tons of ore a year.

At the time of his death C.P. Markham was chairman and managing direc-tor of Staveley Coal & Iron Company Ltd, Parkgate Iron & Steel Company Ltd, Markham Main Collieries Ltd, Bullcroft Main Collieries, Newstead Colliery Company Ltd, Yorkshire Main Colliery Ltd, British Soda Company Ltd, Doncaster Collieries Association Ltd, Midland Ironstone Company Ltd,

Burton Limestone Company Ltd, Cranford Ironstone Company Ltd and Loddington Ironstone Company Ltd, Eastwell Iron Ore Company, and Lamport Ironstone Company; until 1925 he had been chairman and managing director of Markham & Company. Markham was also joint managing director of Brodsworth Main Colliery Company Ltd with his younger brother Arthur, and a director of Ramcroft Colliery Company Ltd, Hickleton Main Colliery Company Ltd, Firbeck Main Collieries Company Ltd (owned jointly with the Sheepbridge Company), the Industrial Housing Association Ltd, Chesterfield Housing Company Ltd and the Housing Association Ltd.

Markham & Co. 1889 to 1901

C.P. Markham acquired Broad Oaks works from the receiver of Oliver's in 1889 and named the firm Markham & Co. Within twelve years the workforce increased to 600 and the products of the company led to his boast that a fifth of all the coal mined in Britain was brought to the surface by equipment manufactured in Chesterfield.

During the period from 1889 to 1900 Markham put in hand developments to extend and improve Broad Oaks works. The river Rother was diverted to enable the workshops to be extended northwards and a culvert built from the

11 Ten Price TBMs for the London Underground.

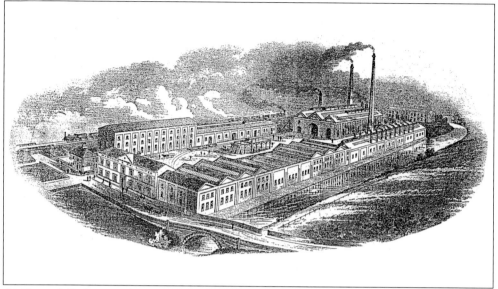

12 Broad Oaks works in 1895.

weir to maintain the water supply to the Midland Railway water tower near
the station. The fitting, erecting and machine shops were extended and a new
boiler shop was built. Steam heating was installed for the machine shop
though the rest of the works used braziers. Two 500 hp by 160 lb/sq in. steam
engines and generators were built for in-house electricity generation at 110
volts. The total installed generating capacity was eventually one 500 kw set,
one 300 kw set and two 150 kw sets. The shops were also served with a
compressed air main at 100 lb/sq in. and a water hydraulic main at 1,500
lb/sq in. The structural department shops had four steam forging hammers,
a smithy with 20 fires and a linear bank of 12 radial drills able to cover girders
100 ft long.

Tunnelling shields were required at this time to extend the London underground railway and in this period no fewer than 100 shields and tunnel
boring machines (TBMs) were produced. The TBMs were made to the design
of J. Price, and incorporated a circular rotating excavator or cutting head.
Shields for the London Underground varied in type and size: some were for
single track, some for twin track and others for stations; station shields were
over 25 ft in diameter. Shields were also supplied to the North British Railway
and to the West Middlesex waterworks.

Also during this period 21 mine winders were built of various types, with
single, double and bi-conical drums. They would all have been steam driven.

Locomotives continued to be built for ironstone quarries and for the
Staveley Coal & Iron Co. One of these, built in 1894, was an 0-4-0 saddle tank
engine named Gladys which is preserved at the Midland Railway Centre at

Butterley.

Markham also provided equipment for the Renishaw Iron Works, which was owned by Appleby Walker & Co.

A catalogue published in the 1890s gives an indication of the wide range of engineering products which were being produced at Broad Oaks Works at that time. The list can be summarised as follows: winding engines, with either vertical or horizontal steam cylinders; hauling and hoisting engines; pumping engines; steam engines for driving workshop line shafting; workshop line shafts and pulleys; air compressors; steam pumps; boilers, flues and fittings, including safety, water feed and sluice valves; furnace ventilation fans; shunting locomotives; pit headgear, pulleys, cages and pit washery screens; kibbles, tubs and tub tipplers; girders and structural iron members; hydraulically driven cranes; hot blast stoves and cupolas for ironworks; and rock drill boring machinery.

Markham & Co. 1901 to 1914

During this period C.P. Markham remained chairman of the company but in 1911 C.J. Mawhood was appointed managing director.

Between 1901 and 1914 extensions were made to the fitting shop and twice to the boiler shop and new amenity baths were installed. The 'German' crane was purchased and erected in 1904 to serve the stockyard at the north end of

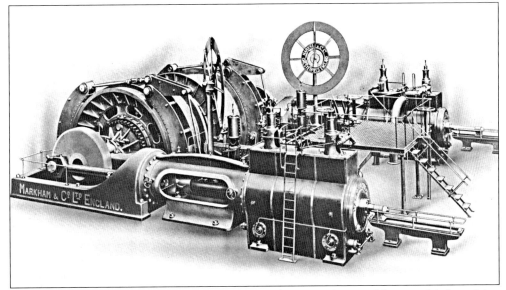

13 A pair of 40 × 72 in. semi-Corliss winding engines with two 14 ft × 6 in. parallel drums for South Africa.

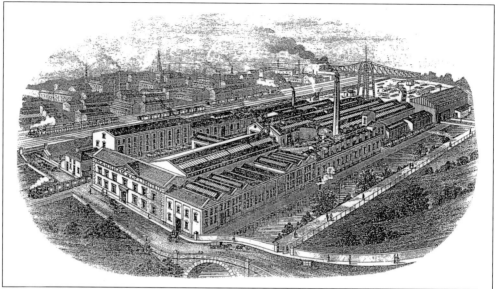

14 Broad Oaks works in 1914.

the works, particularly the foundry where a portion of the roof could be lifted off. The German crane was of double cantilever design, 120 ft high with a lifting capacity of 16 tons at a radius of 30 ft and 5 tons at 60 ft radius; the height under the fully raised hook was 90 ft. It could traverse 240 ft along a railway track and became a landmark in Chesterfield.

Tunnelling equipment formed a major part of business undertaken in this period. A total of 113 shields and TBMs were supplied, mainly for extending the London Underground. Two pilot shields and two main shields, each of 30 ft 8 in (9.4m) diameter and weighing 425 tons, were supplied for the Rother-hithe tunnel under the river Thames in east London. Other equipment supplied for this project in 1905 and 1906 included bulkheads, arches, girders, caissons and shaft chambers. In 1906 two shields were supplied for driving the Paris metro tunnels, as well as shields for the London Underground and nine shields for the General Post Office underground railway at Mount Pleasant.

A total of 61 mine winders were built during the period, which included the first electric winder, built for British Westinghouse. The winder installation at Yorkshire Main colliery supplied in 1905 also included the complete surface equipment, including the headgear and associated buildings. The winding drum was of the bi-conical type and was one of the largest ever built.

Other significant products supplied during the period included hydraulic pumping engines for John Brown & Co. of Sheffield, later to become Firth Brown, which were still working in 1972; power station engines to drive electricity generators for Newport tramways in South Wales; five hot blast stoves for Parkgate Iron & Steel Co. of 21 ft 6 in. diameter and 75 ft high; an

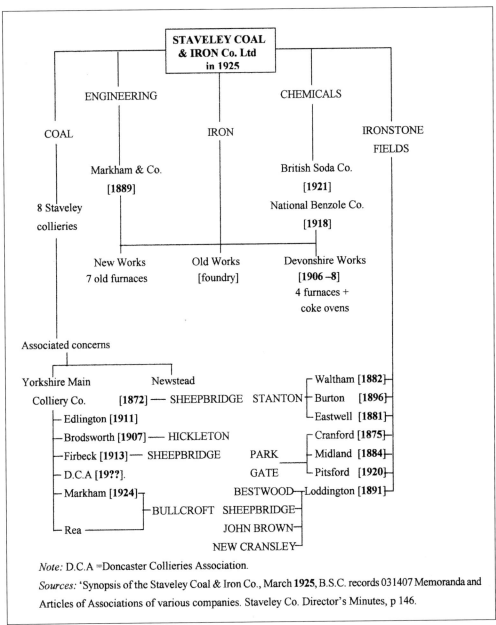

15 Staveley Coal and Iron Co., its principal activities and its associated companies in 1925.

electrically driven slab charger for a carriage and wagon works in Manchester; eight headgear pulleys for South Africa; a blowing engine for the Japanese navy; the first haulage engines for coal mines, including a 300 hp electrically driven main and tail haulage; two shipbuilding cranes; and a plate rolling mill including steelwork and roof together with Wellman-type furnaces.

Markham & Co. during the First World War

During the war the manufacture of mine winders continued, with eight being supplied to British collieries. Extensive on site maintenance was also undertaken.

Eight 6ft diameter 'attack' excavator shields were made for the War Office for use by the Sappers in France in order to tunnel under the German trenches. It is not known whether some or all of the machines were used since delivery may have been too late for the hostilities.

Other war work involved the collaboration with other companies involved in the war effort. This included the supply of presses and accumulators for Davy Brothers of Sheffield; three rolling mill engines produced for Beardmore, Parkgate Iron & Steel and Colvilles, and a complete rolling mill for Baldwins; gas producers for Vickers; and a nitro benzol plant for Staveley.

Primary works production included ten 750 ton shell presses, thirteen 500 ton shell presses, four triple expansion marine engines for the Admiralty, and blast furnaces for Parkgate Iron & Steel and Staveley.

Additionally during 1916 the Broad Oaks blast furnaces on Derby Road were brought under Markham management.

Markham & Co. 1918 to 1924

This post-war period was the last phase of C.P. Markham's ownership. The company was sold to Staveley Coal & Iron in 1924 for £5,000. W.C. Macartney was appointed managing director in mid 1927 on the retirement of C.J. Mawhood.

A 1.5-ton electric arc furnace was constructed for internal use and a 2.5-ton experimental electric locomotive was built and tests carried out.

A total of 64 tunnelling shields were supplied during the period, most of them for extensions to the London Underground system.

Re-equipping of the coalmines was urgently needed after the war, and 27 winders were supplied during the period. Also six Lancashire boilers were supplied to Markham Main colliery at Armthorpe near Doncaster.

Markham was aware that coalmine mechanisation would extend to the replacement of pit ponies and in 1917 the design and development of a range of mechanical hauling engines to move loads underground by rope attached to wagons was put in hand. These hauling engines were designated Pony, Mule and Stallion in the order of their three different power ratings. In 1919 it was decided to establish a workshop dedicated to the manufacture of these hauling engines and the name 'hauling shop' remained until closure of the works. The range included single and double drum alternatives with steam, electric or compressed air driven options. Over 1,000 hauling engines were made over the first five-year period.

16 The Rotherhithe Tunnel shield, rear view.

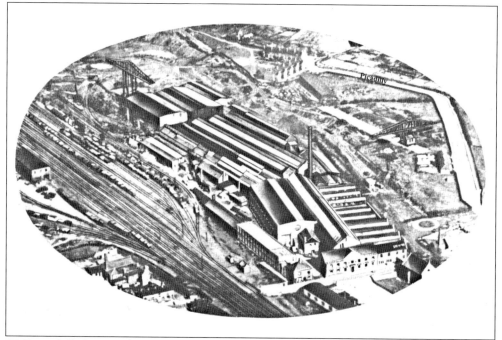

17 Broad Oaks works in 1933.

Staveley Coal & Iron Co. Ltd, owners of Markham & Co. from 1924 to 1937

The modern history of ironmaking at Staveley began in 1840 when Richard Barrow took over the works, which had been in use on the same site since the early seventeenth century. Production in the period immediately prior to 1840 was principally iron bars and plates, rollers, stoves, chimney backs and shot and shells. When Barrow arrived the works employed 500 people in coalmines, ironworks and administration. The company produced 50,000 tons of coal and 5,000 tons of iron castings a year.

Barrow concentrated production on pipes and columns and the works was reorganised and expanded when Charles Markham took over as managing director. The company was incorporated as the Staveley Coal and Iron Co. Ltd in 1864 and by the following year annual production had increased to 780,000 tons of coal and 22,900 tons of iron castings. Henry Pochin, who took over as chairman from Richard Barrow, said 'we probably have the largest iron casting business in the country, and perhaps in the world'. By that time, coal output was 800,000 tons and iron castings 30,000 tons per year.

Subsequently the works was extended and developed to cover an area of over 200 acres, with blast furnaces, coke ovens, chemical plant and foundries manufacturing cast iron pipes, columns, girders, plates, coal mine shaft 'tubbing', tunnel lining segments and castings of all types. The company owned eight collieries with a total coal output just before the First World War of 4 million tons a year. Pig iron output was 365,000 tons and some 17,000 people were employed.

In 1947 the plant was changed radically under nationalisation.

By 2002 the 'old' and 'new' works were closed and demolished. The company is now named Staveley Industries plc and their head office is in Croydon.

18 Blast furnace plant at Staveley works entirely equipped by Markham.

Markham & Co. 1924 to 1937

The period 1924 to 1937 saw Markham & Co. Ltd under Staveley Coal & Iron Company ownership. C.P. Markham died in 1926 leaving Markham well established in the mining and tunnelling industries and as a principal and respected mechanical engineering supplier. In 1931 the directors were D.N. Turner (chairman), W.C. McCartney (managing), H. Barnes, H.H. Berresford and P.A. Welby. Frank Williams was the works manager and J. Cook the company secretary.

In order to expand Markham products an agreement was signed with Boving and Co. Ltd for Markham to manufacture waterpower equipment to Boving designs. The first water turbines were built in 1929.

During the period 56 winders were supplied which included 31 supplied to the developing South African gold mines, the largest to Randfontein Estate mine.

The hauling shop was extended to provide an increased output of 800 units a year. Hauling engines were built for stock, enabling the company to offer virtually immediate delivery. For example, 43 engines of various types and size were delivered in February 1927 and at this time Markham was the

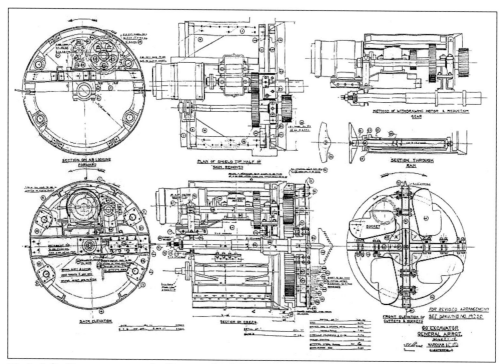

19 A 6 ft diameter attack digger shield: a significant contribution by Markham to the engineering history of the First World War.

largest producer of hauling engines in the country.

A total of 111 tunnelling shields and TBMs were supplied, including 30 for the London Underground and large shields for the first Mersey tunnel and for the first Dartford to Purfleet tunnel under the river Thames.

A 6.6m diameter shield was built for the Moscow metro. The use of shields for tunnelling was a new concept for the Russians and turned out to be a favourite of the project director Nikita Kruschev. A number of identical shields were constructed in the USSR for use on the Moscow metro. Shields were also built for the Barcelona metro, for the Trinidad waterworks and for the Calabro–Lucana railway in Italy.

Markham built a spun cast-iron pipe plant for the Staveley Group under a USA 'Sand Spun' licence. The plant was built and installed between 1929 and 1931. Also in 1931 Markham fulfilled a structural steel contract for a record, for them, of 1,500 tons of girder work for a building reconstruction at Baker Street, London.

In 1937 Markham & Co. was purchased by John Brown & Co. Ltd. for £50,000. Eric Mensforth became general manager having persuaded John Brown to purchase Markham so as to have a secure supplier of structural steelwork for his new employers, Westland Aircraft of Yeovil.

20 Rolling mill housings made by Markham.

21 Shield for the first Mersey Tunnel.

John Brown & Co. Ltd, owners of Markham for 49 years, 1937–96

(Sir) John Brown (1816–91) started his own manufacturing business in Orchard Street, Sheffield, in 1844, moving to his new Atlas works in 1856. John Brown & Co. became a limited company in 1864. John Brown took over Firths in 1903 and Thomas Firth & John Brown Ltd was formed in 1930.

John Brown & Co also owned Clydebank Shipyard, Glasgow (1899); John Brown Engineering, Glasgow; Firth Brown Tools, Sheffield; Cravens, Sheffield; John Brown Land Boilers, Scotland; Wickman Machine Tools, Coventry; Constructors John Brown, London; John Brown Plastics; and John Brown Special Engineering and Nuclear Developments (SEND).

Some of the later John Brown directors included Lord Aberconway, the chairman, who was also chairman of Sheepbridge Engineering and English China Clays; Lord Bilsland, who was also a director of Colvilles and the Bank of Scotland; Lord Clitheroe MP, chairman of the Conservative party from 1944 to 1946, and also vice-chairman of Tube Investments, chairman of Borax Consolidated, and a director of Mercantile Investment Trust and the National Provincial Bank; Lord Aldington MP, Minister of State at the Board of Trade from 1954 to 1957, and also a director of GEC, Dorman Long and London Assurance; Sir Eric Mensforth, also chairman of Westland Aircraft; and R.J.

22 Cast-iron segments for the first Mersey Tunnel.

Barclay.

Today John Brown trades as CB&I John Brown Ltd and is still based at 20 Eastbourne Terrace, London. John Brown's owners, Chicago Bridge & Iron Co. N.V. (CB&I) is one of the world's leading engineering, procurement and construction companies, with approximately 11,000 employees. Projects undertaken by John Brown include engineering design, procurement, construction, installation, commissioning and consultancy to both onshore and offshore technology, refining, petrochemical process and pipeline industries in all major areas of the world.

Markham & Co. 1938 to 1958

Eric Mensforth left Markham to join Westland Aircraft as joint managing director to prepare Westland for war production. Robert Barclay joined Markham from English Electric as general manager, later to become managing director.

In 1938 Markham built its last steam winders, for Victoria and Kilnhurst collieries, as well as two electric winders for Easington colliery. Five shields were supplied in 1938. Two double drum winders were exported, one to South Africa and one to Australia in 1939.

Markham production from 1939 to 1945 was dictated by national priorities and by the availability of labour and materials. The company employed more than 1,000 men and women throughout the war. Five winders and one tunnelling shield were built during this period. Early on in the war Markham was awarded a major structural contract to design and install blackout screens for the blast furnaces at Staveley.

Two other projects specifically for the war effort were the production of two X and two XE type miniature submarines (see pp. 61–2) and the manufacture of 31 LCM landing craft for the invasion of mainland Europe.

In 1941 the Spare Shaft Association was formed. Representatives of 44 privately owned colliery companies met Markham staff at Chesterfield and expressed an interest in setting up a central pool of spare shafts to minimise downtime in the event of winder drum shaft failure. Under the auspices of the association draft rules were agreed. At that time a survey had been made and the shaft sizes identified ranged in weight from 10 cwt to 28 tons and in size from 6 in. diameter by 9 ft 7 in. long to 27 in. diameter by 31 ft 8 in. long. The 14 sizes of spare shaft forgings were to be in a rough machined and bored condition and in size categories A to O to cover 220 winders. The shafts were primarily for steam engine driven winders whose shafts could occasionally develop cracks or fractures due to high stresses induced by the piston driven cranks.

After some months had passed the level of interest had grown and when the association came into being 950 different sizes of shaft for 1,000 colliery winders were catered for. Week by week new members joined and ultimately more than 99 per cent of all winders were covered. Markham was chosen as manufacturer and as the storage site for the pool of shafts. The company was also appointed the agent to administer the scheme and answer to an elected management committee. The subscription for each member was on the basis of £3 15s. per ton weight of shafts, which each member declared. Out of the established fund the management committee instructed the agent from time to time to purchase such new shaft forgings as may be required. With limited wartime steel allocations it could take three or four months or more to obtain the requisite forgings.

After the war the need to develop and re-equip the coalmines was a top priority. Three winders had been supplied to Beckwith colliery in 1943 and a fourth was built in 1945 together with a winder for Arkwright colliery. Three winders were built for Mansfield colliery.

Two large vertical boring lathes were brought from Germany and installed as part of post-war reparations. This enabled Germany to get rid of old secondhand machines and to install new ones paid for by the USA Marshall Aid plan! So much for 'winning' the war.

In 1947 a major turnkey project was begun to equip the new Rothes colliery in Fife (see Appendix 6). During the early post-war period winders were

23 A slurry type TBM for Mexico City.

supplied to Clipstone, Dalkeith, Hem Heath, Maltby, Teversall, New Hucknall, Sutton, Bevercotes, Silverhill and Wolstanton collieries as well as two mines in Australia. In all 32 winders and eight tunnelling shields were supplied in the period.

Other projects included water turbines for Owen Falls at the source of the Nile in Uganda and for the Murray river in Australia. A new product developed in this period was a low air pressure stowing machine to ram material, usually mine spoil, into voids underground to support the roof and to channel ventilation air in 'room and pillar' mine workings. This proved to be a very profitable 'bread and butter' product for Markham over the following 20 years until the coal industry changed its operating method to 'retreat' mining. A separate department was established with its own design office and service team.

The company also made three cotton-baling presses for Egypt; the propeller for Sir Donald Campbell's speedboat Bluebird in 1950; and a new weather vane for the crooked spire of Chesterfield parish church in 1951. Markham also participated in the project to install a 100 kW vertical axis wind power generator in the Orkneys designed by Tom Mensforth, Eric's brother.

John Brown & Co. Ltd was undergoing great changes as a result of the nationalisation of the coal and steel industries. Steel and toolmaker Firth

24 Birmingham University radio telescope.

Brown was nationalised, as were the coalmines in the company. John Brown was obliged to develop new business outside these sectors.

By 1958 Markham had over 1,000 employees to cope with this boom period after the war when a sellers' market prevailed.

Markham & Co. 1958 to 1968

R.J. Barclay (known as RJB in the company) was appointed a director of John Brown and became deputy chairman of Markham. Eric Mensforth became chairman and George Hand the managing director. Barclay and Mensforth were contemporaries at Cambridge, and Markham designed, built and installed a large low-speed research wind tunnel, largely made of wood, on the top floor of the University Engineering laboratory on Trumpington Street. This was Barclay's 'hobby' contract and Mike Bennett, then chief engineer, spent very many weekends with RJB in Cambridge during the protracted installation, much to the annoyance of Mike's wife, who had to look after their two young children. This was not the first wind tunnel in which Markham was involved. In 1931 they erected 'the great density tunnel' (a high pressure wind tunnel) at the National Physical Laboratory at Teddington for John Brown & Co. The company also built a water tunnel at Haslar, near Portsmouth.

During this period Mike Bennett became Markham's first technical director, having replaced Desmond Lear as chief engineer in 1964.

The reduction in the number of collieries during the rationalisation carried out by Lord Robens as chairman of the National Coal Board resulted in appreciably less business for Markham. The stowing business continued at a constant level but only eleven winders were built in the period. These were for Rufford, Newstead, Shirebrook, Daw Mill, Horden and Manton collieries.

Simple tunnelling shields and structural steelwork were no longer within Markham's competitive price range since the burgeoning water turbine business increased the hourly rate for fabrication and Markham did not apply a differential overhead. The tunnelling industry perceived Markham as a supplier only for larger shields and TBMs, which were beyond the capability

25 AGR refuelling machine on the pile cap at the UKAEA establishment at Windscale. The machine weighed 430 tons and positioned itself over a reactor standpipe to within 0.005 in.

26 The AGR refuelling machine SEND team. Left to right: Stan Howarth, a UKAEA inspector, Malcolm — , Laurie Jones, Eric Walters, Ken Wort, Eric Langham.

of the cheaper competition.

New developments were taking place in tunnelling technology as a result of the greater variety of ground which TBMs were required to tackle. Tunnels were being driven through water-bearing strata, which meant that the rotating cutting head had to operate in a sealed front chamber. Various means were used to remove the excavated spoil from the chamber one being the so-called 'slurry' method. The spoil was 'slurrified' by an agitator using ground water and a bentonite solution introduced into the chamber, which was pumped out, carrying the spoil, and transferred to the surface by pipeline. In 1967 Markham received an order from a civil engineering plant contractor, Anglo-Scottish Plant, to design and supply three 6m diameter slurry TBMs for a sewer project in Mexico City.

Another special engineering development was the invention by Dr Bronowski of the NCB of a new system for making coal dust and cement briquettes. Markham won the order to supply the prototype briquette press from the NCB.

The water turbine business from Boving now formed a significant proportion of the total order book. This work well suited Markham providing

27 The AGR refuelling machine Markham works team and SEND. Left to right: Eric Walters, Ken Wort, Jack Reynolds, — , Denis Crich, Harry Lacey, Monty Harrold, — , George Davis, Mick Power, Stan Howarth.

a good balance for the fabrication, machining and fitting shops. Furthermore there were no marketing costs, delivery time was generous, there was no design risk, and it was commercially rewarding. Particular projects in this period were six large Francis turbines for the Kariba Dam in Rhodesia and in Spain two Kaplan turbines each for Velle, Castrello and Friera, and two pump turbines for Villarino.

Markham had a good relationship with Husband & Co. who were consulting engineers based in Sheffield. In 1959 an order was received for the azimuth and elevation machinery for the 100 ft diameter Goonhilly GPO radio telescope at Land's End and in 1968 orders were received for two steerable aerials to the overall design of Husband & Co. One was for the GPO research establishment at Martlesham Heath near Ipswich and the other was for Birmingham University to be installed on the roof of one of its buildings. Detail design, other than for the 20 ft diameter dishes, was carried out by Markham.

Sir Charles Husband also involved Markham in the manufacture of a replacement for a cracked stone beam supporting the landing of one of the rear staircases at Chatsworth House. This was actually made in steel,

28 Self-advancing roadway support for the National Coal Board.

fabricated to the exact complex cross-section of the original, and cleverly disguised with stone coloured texture paint to be indistinguishable from the stone beam which it replaced.

Orders also flowed from within the much diversified John Brown Group. John Brown had formed a consortium with the Foster Wheeler Corporation to build coal-fired power stations and the coal pulverising mills for power stations at Eggborough, Ironbridge, Aberthaw and Rugeley were made by Markham. Following an explosion of pulverised fuel inside a coal pulverising mill at Tilbury B power station Markham were commissioned to design and manufacture strengthening for the casings of the Tilbury mills.

Constructors John Brown in London was venturing into offshore work and Markham built a submersible work chamber for them for the inspection of underwater structures.

With the advent of the nuclear age John Brown set up a nuclear division at their Paddington offices initially with the intention of forming a consortium with another UK engineering group to bid for nuclear power station work.

29 Shield used for the construction of the second Dartford Tunnel.

This division, later to become John Brown Special Engineering and Nuclear Developments (SEND), and comprising a design engineering and marketing arm for the group, bid for and secured the order for the design, supply and installation of the reactor refuelling machine for the UKAEA Advanced Gas Cooled reactor (AGR) at Windscale, now called Sellafield, in Cumberland. This very complex and very successful machine was designed to refuel the reactor whilst it was on load, the only one in the world to do so. It had to position itself on the reactor pile cap within 0.005 in. over any of the 253 reactor stand pipes which contained the fuel rods, and over the other 27 facilities on the reactor operating floor.

The machine weighed 430 tons and stood over 60 ft high. It was built at Markham and the fitters and riggers who had built it erected it on site within the dome shaped AGR containment building.

The refuelling machine project was masterminded by Robert Barclay; the machine was designed by John Brown SEND with Ken Wort as their man supervising construction, site installation and commissioning, with Mike Bennett recruited from the UKAEA supervising works erection. Mike also

30 Broad Oaks works in the 1980s.

designed the machine's cooling system.

John Brown SEND Ltd introduced Markham to DEMAG (later Mannessman DEMAG) of Duisburg in West Germany. Several hundred tons of run out equipment was made by Markham for DEMAG universal beam rolling mills for South Durham Steel & Iron and Shelton steel works.

John Brown purchased the rights to the Gebrüder Pfeiffer MPS type vertical spindle roller mill, which they vested in PHI Engineering Ltd, a member of the group. Mills for pulverising coal at a number of cement works were built at Markham.

Another significant contract was awarded to Markham through J.M.J. Maus Ltd of Hammersmith, agents for Fried Krupp of Wilhelmshaven. A new technique in the construction of large ships was to prefabricate large sections, which were manoeuvred into position by very large, high capacity goliath cranes. Markham secured the order for the manufacture and erection of the shear leg for an 810-ton goliath crane for Harland and Wolff of Belfast. The site work was undertaken at a very difficult period in the Northern Ireland Troubles, and the crane became an instantly recognisable feature of the Belfast skyline.

The Hope cement works of APCM was under construction in 1967 and Markham secured the order for the manufacture of the kiln base plates and for the assembly of base plates and bearings from Polysius, a Krupp subsidiary. The base plate assemblies were each over 40 tons in weight and special transport arrangements had to be made through the Peak District country roads.

A number of attempts were made to develop a product range. These included a packaging machine, Techite pipe, a tungsten carbide lined flail type crusher producing granite road stone, and a hydraulic brake for mine winders.

Markham & Co. 1968 to 1988

George Hand retired in 1968 and Bill Taylor, who had been recruited from F.H. Lloyd, the steel founder based at Jamesbridge, Darlaston, replaced him. Bill Taylor was a works man through and through. He had started his working life in a metallurgical laboratory and progressed to be works manager of F.H. Lloyd. He was familiar with the Markham water turbine business since Lloyds had been a major supplier to Markham of stainless steel turbine castings for many years. Bill was a Walsall man, as was Ken Wort who joined Markham from John Brown SEND after the AGR refuelling machine became operational. Ken was to become commercial director. Bill settled happily in

31 Cairo waste water scheme TBM.

32 One of two Channel Tunnel TBMs, showing one-eighth of its total length.

Holymoorside and Ken in Brampton.

The mine winder business was given a boost in 1978 with the start of the NCB Plan for Coal. Prior to that only two hoists had been built in the period, a slope hoist for Cape Breton in Canada and a replacement drum for the one damaged in the disaster at Markham colliery. To gear up for the Plan for Coal business, Thyssen GB ordered three double-drum clutched sinking winders between 1978 and 1980 aimed at securing, as they did, shaft sinking work for the new Selby mine. Orders for five six-rope friction winders for the Selby mine were received from the NCB in 1981 and 1985. Markham also built for Cable Belt Ltd the 13,000 hp drive head unit and friction wheels for the conveyor belt at the Selby mine Gascoigne Wood drift.

Fifteen more winder orders, required for the Plan for Coal, were delivered in the period together with five single-drum emergency winders. Two winders were supplied to South Africa and five to NEI for the State Gold mines in Ghana.

In 1970 the foundry was closed and converted into a light fabrication shop

33 The Channel Tunnel TBM back-up system.

and the blacksmith and forging operations were phased out. New numerically controlled machines and NC conversion of some existing machines were introduced in the 1970s.

A self-advancing mine roadway support was developed and successful trials of the prototype took place at Ollerton colliery. Nine units were then delivered to the NCB consisting of two basic designs., self-advancing and advanceable.

The period was also noted for tunnelling machinery deliveries. In 1970 a shield and a drum type digger were built for Anglo-Scottish Plant. The drum digger was used on the Barcelona metro construction.

In 1970 Mike Bennett left the company. In 1979 he founded an engineering design and procurement company, Skeltonhall Ltd, and in 1984 founded a consulting engineering company M.G. Bennett & Associates: both companies carried out design work for Markham. Ken Randon succeeded him as Markham's technical director.

In 1972 Markham supplied three shields to Charles Brand for the London Underground Fleet line development, later to be called the Jubilee line. The company also manufactured and works test assembled a temporary road deck to cover the new station construction beneath the Oxford Street and Bond Street intersection to keep traffic moving during the tunnel construction period. The deck weighed over 400 tons and was erected in 48 hours on site.

34 The bridge deck at Bond Street Underground station.

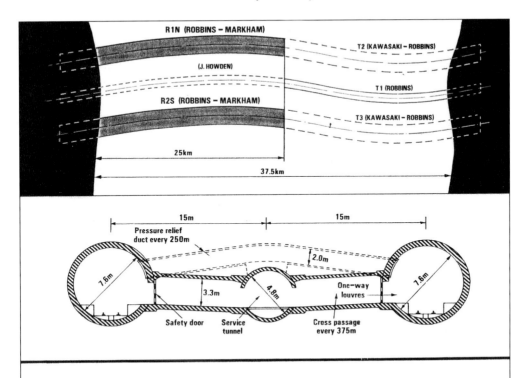

Specification for 2—Running Tunnel machines for Channel Tunnel UK Maritime Drivage.

Cut diameter	8.36m		No. of segment erectors	2 upper & 2 lower
Cutters alternatively	276 Rocking Picks 58 discs		Segment delivery system	1 upper slat conveyor 1 lower conveyor
Cutterhead torque	5.25×10^6 NM		Fire fighting system	2 foam plugs 2 water curtains AFFF units Hand appliances
Cutterhead speed	2.2 to 3.3 rpm			
Cutterhead drive	12×110 kW Water cooled clutched electric motors		No. of back-up sledges	13
Number and stroke of advance rams	20×1500mm		Electrical supply voltage	11,000/415v
			Total installed power	2.3 mW
Installed thrust to cutterhead	4220 tonne		Emergency battery	900 ah
Number and stroke of auxiliary thrust rams	16×2000mm		Water pumps	2×150 1/sec inrush 1×40 1/sec circulation 1×50 1/sec discharge
Installed thrust of auxiliary rams	470 tonne		Ventilation system	300 m³/min incoming 250 m³/min extracted
No. of gripper shoes	4		Probe drills	2 DIAMEC 260
Ground pressure from gripper (normal)	18.5 bar		Machine weight (approx.)	1350 tonne
No. of conveyors	3		Machine length (overall)	250m
Conveyor capacity	1500 tph			

35 Specification of the Channel Tunnel TBMs and an overview of the project.

In 1973 two 10.5 m. diameter shields were built for Balfour Beatty for driving the second Dartford tunnel under the Thames. Each shield weighed 365 tonnes and Markham personnel erected the shields on site. The shields were equipped with hydraulically operated excavating arms.

The advent of high-pressure hydraulic systems enabled tunnelling shields to be equipped with powerful back acters to undertake powered excavation and so accelerate tunnelling rates. Shields of this type for use with standard 100 in. expanded concrete linings were delivered to Thyssen GB and to Miller Buckley for tunnelling projects in Buckinghamshire and London respectively. Four shields incorporating boom type rotary excavators to deal with harder ground were delivered to John Mowlem for the Carsington reservoir water tunnels in Derbyshire and for the Benwell sewer project at Newcastle-upon-Tyne.

TBMs for rock excavation were designed and built for Lodigiani in Italy for a water tunnel scheme at Taormina in Sicily and for Fairclough for a water tunnel at Halifax. The Halifax machine was designed for use with a 2 m. outside diameter pipe jacked tunnel lining and was the first hard rock machine specifically built for pipe jacking in the UK.

In 1985 the Cairo Wastewater scheme financed through British loans was begun. The tunnels were to be driven through wet sandy ground and slurry type TBMs were specified. A technical licence agreement was signed with the Okumura Corporation of Osaka, Japan, who produced the machine design. Three slurry type TBMs were manufactured at Markham and shipped to Cairo for the tunnelling contractors, Lilley of Glasgow. Two were of 5.2 m. and one of 6.2 m. diameter. All were equipped with crushers to deal with boulders.

In order to increase the capacity of the works at the heavy end of the business two bays of the erecting shop were extended and equipped with 100 ton capacity cranes in the mid 1980s. This development was perfectly timed for the 1987 Channel Tunnel TBM contract for the supply of two TBMs for the two running (rail) tunnels for the sub sea construction of the Channel Tunnel. This contract was signed by the Robbins Markham Joint Venture with the UK consortium of contractors Trans-Manche Link. Bennett Associates was retained to design the back-up system comprising the muck disposal and concrete tunnel lining segment delivery and build systems and services such as air and water supply.

Other tunnelling projects in this period included the supply of two jacking shields for the NCB for pit bottom development at the new Asfordby mine in Leicestershire and a back-up system for a mining project for AMCO of Barnsley. Again Bennett Associates assisted with the design.

A completely different project, in 1970, was the construction of two 2,500 tonne block presses for the manufacture of carbon anodes for the ALBA aluminium smelter in Bahrain. For this work collaboration with a specialist company was again essential: Von Roll of Klus, Switzerland, was specified and

36 Two friction winders for Asfordby colliery.

an agreement was concluded with them. Subsequently, in order to improve production, larger press moulds were built and fitted at site. Later, an order for a conveyor to handle aluminium slabs was received. This was designed by Bennett Associates and was manufactured and successfully commissioned by Markham.

John Brown was taken over by the Trafalgar House group in 1986 and a new set of sister companies came into being, including Cleveland Bridge, CEMCO and Cunard. Cable Belt Ltd placed an order for a 13,000 hp gearbox for a Canadian mine conveyor belt. Other notable work in the period included the manufacture and erection of 15 slurry agitators to the design of Fried Krupp of Rheinhausen, Germany, for the Northfleet, Swanscombe and Ockendon works of APCM. The agitators were used to stir and aerate cement slurry inside concrete tanks of 80 ft inside diameter and 46 ft in height. Markham built the turbine assemblies for the Dinorwic pumped storage scheme in north Wales (see p. 69). For PHI Engineering Ltd the company made six MPS 140 coal pulverising mills to provide fuel for the Northfleet

37 Thames Barrier gate trunnions.

38 Cable belt 13,000 hp gearbox.

cement kilns; supplied and installed an MPS 4500 raw meal pulverising mill, weighing 600 tonne, for Irish Cement Platin works at Drogheda; and built 16 MPS 140 coal pulverising mills for Indian power plants.

For DEMAG of Germany Markham made slab yard roller tables and transfer cars for the continuous casting plant at the British Steel Corporation's Scunthorpe works; continuous casting machines for Round Oak Steel works, Staffordshire, and for for Manchester Steel; ladle restoppering stations for BSC Scunthorpe and Llanwern; and lance carriages for BSC Normanby Park.

Work for Wellman included three 200 tonne capacity LD steel making vessels for BSC Normanby Park, while for Vickers Markham made aircraft wheel and tyre dynamometers for Dunlop, the USSR and China, and North Sea oilrig tether anchors and test rig.

Contracts for the Ministry of Defence included stern and bow torpedo tubes for 'O' class submarines, body gauges for checking torpedo handling in submarines, and Trident submarine parts for torpedo handling. Markham also manufactured shielding for nuclear processing plant for Magnox and AGR fuel for British Nuclear Fuels Ltd. For Cleveland Bridge the company machined the trunnion shafts and assembled the trunnion bearings for the Thames Barrier gates. For Clearing Ltd Markham manufactured mechanical

39 The directors in front of the Channel Tunnel cutter head. Left to right: Malcolm Lindley, Nick Bristow, John Ormston, David Walker and Ken Wort.

presses for the motor industry. Finally, for Sindra Smidgeon of Reykjavik the company made a water turbine penstock bifurcation to a patent Krupp design.

Trafalgar House, owners of Markham 1986 to 1996

The Trafalgar House Group started in property development after the Second World War and for a time owned the *Daily Express* newspaper company. By 1994 it employed 36,000 people and had a turnover of £3.9 billion but only turning in a profit, before extraordinary items, of £78 million. The engineering division employed 23,000 and had a turnover of £2.5 billion. Group companies in the UK included Trafalgar House Construction, Cleveland Bridge, Cementation, Trollope & Colls (including T.H. Services Ltd and T.H. Property Ltd), the Ritz Hotel, London, Cunard Steamship Company plc, Ideal Homes, T.H. Offshore Fabrications, Davy of Sheffield, Davy Power Gas, Davy Roll Co., John Brown Construction, John Brown Engineering (which included Markham), John Brown Plastics, and Govan Shipyard. Overseas group companies included Sofresid and Clecim in France and 50 per cent of Gammon

40 A coal pulverising mill made for PHI Engineering Ltd.

41 A 2,500 tonne anode press produced in 1970 to the design of Von Roll of Switzerland for an aluminium smelter in Bahrain.

(HongKong), and the Mandarin Oriental Hotel, Hong Kong.

Trafalgar House ran into financial problems in the mid 1990s, partly due to the Davy Power Gas Emerald Offshore Rig contract, and they were taken over by Kvaerner.

Kvaerner, owners of Markham from 1996 to 1998

Kvaerner is a Norwegian group, established in the 1960s, with interests in shipbuilding, ship repairing, offshore oil and gas and power engineering amongst others. They acquired Trafalgar House in 1996 but due to financial difficulties soon found it necessary to dispose of the civil engineering construction interests to Skanska of Sweden and the oil and gas business with the John Brown name to Yukos of Russia. The Boving water turbine business, which they had also acquired, was sold to GE of the USA. The power division of Kvaerner was reorganised and the Markham business was transferred from Chesterfield to the metals division based at what were the Davy workshops in Sheffield.

Markham & Co. manufacturing between 1988 and 1998

Bill Taylor retired in 1988 and John Ormston, previously managing director of Jenkins of Retford, was appointed as managing director. Nick Bristow joined the company as technical director.

The Channel Tunnel TBMs were in use for three years and were interred in concrete in mid channel to allow the French TBMs to achieve breakthrough in 1991. Robbins Markham service crews were in constant attendance throughout the drivage period. Thereafter until the closure of the Broad Oaks works in 1998 a further 21 shields and TBMs were built. Some were to Markham design whilst Robbins designed others. One of the machines was made under licence from Kawasaki of Japan. In this final period five winders were built for Canada and a further four were refurbished in the works for Harworth colliery and for projects in Turkey and Ghana.

Major water turbine projects included the Vidalia turbines for the USA. The manufacture of these very large turbines had to be dovetailed in with the Channel Tunnel TBMs and all were delivered on time, a notable achievement.

The Government was funding renewable energy development projects at this time and discussions were held with Professor Salter of Heriot-Watt University with a view to Markham building his offshore wave energy 'nodding Duck'. Unfortunately he failed to secure funding beyond the design stage. John Laing was also interested in the use of giant flywheels for storing energy produced intermittently by renewable energy systems. Again Markham

42 Channel Tunnel TBM cutter head. The head could be laced with tungsten carbide spade-type picks or with disc cutters to deal with harder rock. The angled steering rams can be seen.

hoped to build these but this scheme also died the death.

Another renewable energy project involved an agreement with Pehr Wind Technology, an Austrian company, to manufacture wind turbines to their Floda design. Markham had previously been involved with VAWT, a subsidiary of Sir Robert McAlpine, in the manufacture of parts of an 850 kW vertical axis wind turbine. Markham supplied the rotor beam, which was 35m. long. The turbine was ordered under a government development contract and was installed at the CEGB test site at Carmarthen Bay. During trials the turbine suffered damage to its blades and was dismantled. The tests indicated that the design of the vertical axis turbine was not economic.

The Floda wind turbine was of the horizontal axis type with three variable pitch blades and a 'nameplate' output of 600 kW. Two turbines were ordered. One was supplied to a private developer in Sicily, the other to Sir Jack Hayward's Dunmaglass estate in Scotland. This latter turbine suffered damage during erection and a court case ensued. Sir Jack Hayward conceded and requested that the turbine be completed and commissioned.

43 Floda wind turbine assembly.

In 1995 Markham decided to develop an improved version of the Pehr wind turbine incorporating the latest pulse width modulation inverter generator control, which they named the VS 45. A prototype was built and erected for trials on the test site at Wilhelmshaven in Germany. With the decline of the UK market the turbine and design rights for the VS 45 were sold to Windmaster of Holland who subsequently went into liquidation.

Another abortive project was for the supply of a refurbished mine hoist for the proposed underground rock evaluation laboratory for the radioactive nuclear waste storage facility which NIREX were expecting to develop on their site near Gosforth in West Cumbria. NIREX had purchased an ex-NCB winder from Littleton colliery and stored it at Markham. Tenders for the refurbishment and installation of the winder had been accepted when the Government cancelled the project.

The decision in 1998 by Kvaerner that Markham should become part of their metals group led to the closure of Broad Oaks works, with the design department and a number of machine tools being transferred to the Davy Metals site in Sheffield. A few of the works, sales and administration personnel also went to Davy Metals.

44 Round Oak steelworks run-out gear.

What has happened to Markham & Co. since 1998?

On 3 July 1997 the announcement was made that the Broad Oak Works in Chesterfield was to close and key personnel were to be transferred to the Kvaerner Metal Works, Prince of Wales Road, Sheffield. Between then and June 1998 there was a gradual transfer of all departments to Sheffield, though not all those offered jobs were prepared to go. Only 130 people transferred, including most of the design team, a number of the sales force, contract engineers, the tunnelling and mining special products departments, two members from the accounts department, and platers, fitters and machinists. The fabrication shop moved in its entirety and a new layout was planned by Pete Nixon. The large horizontal borers and two large vertical lathes were transferred to Darnall. These take up a great deal of the shop floor originally used for assembly and as a consequence machine-tool beds have to be used on occasion for assembly work. Broad Oaks Works was closed and put up for sale.

Davy became part of Kvaerner Metals but suffered when Kvaerner got into difficulties and the prestigious offices on Prince of Wales Road were closed. Only the Darnall works remained in operation. Kvaerner Process Technology, formerly John Brown, was sold to the Russian firm of Yukos. John Brown is

45 Cement slurry agitators at APCM's Northfleet works.

now under American ownership. Sir John Brown, a Sheffield man, would have been amazed. There was a sub-division of Kvaerner Metals called Markham Tunnelling, which operated for a time though it did not build any machines to its own design. The Markham design team, under the leadership of Mike Robotham, has carried out a number of interesting projects, including a 3,000 hp double-drum winder for Ashanti Gold Fields, Ghana; cable turntables for Pirelli; a radiation shield door for BNFL; test and training rigs for the Royal Navy, Devonport; an 8,000 hp 5.8 m. diameter double-drum winder for Quebec Province, Canada; the operating system and hinge assemblies, in conjunction with Bennett Associates, for the Gateshead Millennium Bridge; the Swing Bridge at Selby; and a novel 'Helix' bridge and a hydraulic jack operated bridge, both for Canary Wharf, London.

At a senior management meeting held on 18 March 2003 it was decreed that the names Kvaerner Markham and Markham Tunnelling were no longer to be used as trade names and thus came to an end the once great name of Markham & Co., after some 117 years. C.P. Markham would have revolved in his grave at some speed that morning! We are told that Kvaerner Markham still exists as a dormant company with two directors, Mike Robotham and Gary Pickering. The main company trades under the name AK Heavy

46 Markham up for sale!

Engineering Co. Ltd.

The Broad Oaks works site was eventually sold to property developers and rumours circulated of its use for a new Chesterfield Football Club ground or a supermarket and retail outlets. At the time of writing some 250 houses and flats have been built on the site. The facade of the original workshops facing the river Rother has been incorporated into one of the blocks of flats, named The Foundry, which have been marketed as 'live-work units' (i.e. flats incorporating office or craft workshop space).

The office block adjoining Hady Hill is grade II listed as is the gatehouse, though the latter hardly seems fit for such an accolade. The main building has been divided into suites of offices occupied by several small businesses.

Products and markets

Markham involvement in the Second World War

When R.J. Barclay was appointed managing director the war had begun and the company was making gun barrel turning lathes and rifling machines for Cravens Ltd, who were a sister company. Markham were also making extrusion presses for Loewy, and it is interesting to note that a large proportion of the aluminium pressings for the war effort came off these machines. Markham made one press a month for thirteen months. Further contributions to the war effort as far as aluminium production was concerned came from two aluminium rolling mills manufactured by Markham. Shortly afterwards the company was designated an Admiralty production unit and continued its long association with the Admiralty first by manufacturing marine engines for small ships and the forward ends of tank landing craft. A little later the company made 31 complete LCMs, which were despatched to the coast from Broad Oaks Works, and four midget submarines

X Craft Miniature Submarines

The X craft miniature submarines were developed in strict secrecy by Varley Marine for the Ministry of Defence. The first six operational submarines were built by Vickers Armstrong and were used in the attack on the German battleship *Tirpitz* in Norwegian waters in 1943. *Tirpitz* was put out of action for the duration of the war but all six X craft were lost.

The Ministry of Defence set three companies in the Midlands to work building twelve more X craft to relieve the load on Vickers submarine yard. Markham of Chesterfield, Broadbent of Huddersfield and Marshall of Gainsborough each built four and collaborated to improve the design. The three companies maintained the highest security in their 'closed shop' production. The intended crew-members came to the works as the craft neared completion to train and add their own personal features. The completed craft were disguised as motor cruisers and shipped by train to Faslane.

R.J. Barclay told the tale of his experience aboard a Vickers-built craft in Loch Striven when he asked if she could dive down to a trial depth of 100 feet. The boat was duly dived but it leaked in many places and RJB got very wet. Needless to say he quickly said 'lets go up again'.

Markham produced X 22 *Exploit*, X 23 *Xiphias*, XE 11 *Lucifer* and XE 12 *Excitable*. The X craft were 15.7 metres long, 1.76 metres in diameter, and weighed 30 tons. With 42 hp diesel engine power and 30 hp battery electric power they had a diving depth of 90 metres, a range of 1,200 miles (towed by a 'big' submarine either submerged or on the surface), and an endurance of seven to ten days. They were armed with two tons of explosives and two containers of limpet mines. The XE craft were slightly larger than X craft and had air conditioning for Far East operations.

Of the four Markham-built X craft, X 22 sank and the four-man crew was lost after being rammed by its towing submarine in the Pentland Firth in 1944. X 23, together with Broadbent's X 20, preceding the Normandy invasion by four days, and captained by Lieut. George Honour, who was awarded the DSC for carrying out the operation, undertook survey duties off the Juno and Sword Normandy beaches and acted as navigation beacons for the D day amphibious allied forces. She was scrapped in 1945. XE 11 sank after surfacing under a boom defence vessel in Lock Striven in 1945, with the loss of three crew-members, and XE 12 was put into reserve at Portsmouth and travelled to Navy Day exhibitions. She was scrapped in 1952.

Two X craft can be seen at museums: X 24, built by Marshall, at the RN Submarine Museum, Gosport, and XE 8, made by Broadbent, at the Imperial War Museum, Duxford.

Other X craft successes were the sinking of the Japanese cruiser *Takao* in the Singapore Naval Base and the cutting of the Singapore–Saigon and Singapore–Hong Kong telegraph cables.

47 Miniature submarine X24 *Expeditious* at Gosport Naval Museum.

Markham winders

From 1869 until 1998, for almost 130 years, Markham designed and built 280 mine winders. Of these, 140, built between 1869 and 1938, were steam engine driven and another 140, built between 1903 and 1998, were electric motor driven.

Winders were of all types including single and double drum, some of them clutched for shaft sinking duty, bi-conical and parallel drum and multi-rope friction winders. Winders were supplied for many duties, such as slope hoists, shaft sinking and emergency hoists. The hoists were mainly for winding men and materials from British coalmines. In 1920 C.P. Markham maintained that 20 per cent of the coal from British mines was brought to the surface by Markham winders.

From the 1930s onwards over 40 winding engines were supplied to gold mines in Africa and others, together with headgear pulleys, were exported to Canada and Australia.

In addition to winders, winches were built for various uses, such as roping up mine shafts, bridge elevation and underground mine haulage for transporting men and materials around the workings.

A range of standard mine haulages, which were optionally either pneumati-

48 Fabricated pulley wheels for mine headgears.

cally or electrically driven, were developed after the First World War.

The winder business required dedicated back-up support and winders were taken out of operation at bank holidays and at the fortnight summer shutdown for maintenance by Markham teams of fitters. Using heavy-duty tackle and working round the clock they refurbished both winders and headgear, fitting spare parts, which had been ordered and manufactured prior to shut down, as required.

Often at the fortnightly summer shutdown a winder would be completely removed and replaced by a new one or one transferred from another site, usually requiring the winder house roof to be removed. This was no mean feat since a hundred or more tons of material had to be handled. Markham's reputation was never to have delayed restarting winding for the men returning from holiday.

Headgear pulleys and deflector sheaves up to the largest size ever made were manufactured and installed from the mid 1860s. Initially headgear pulley rims and bosses were of cast iron construction, as were winder drum sides, bed frames and steam engine parts. Hence there was ample justification for a works iron foundry. The foundry also cast brass and bronze and white metal for the large-diameter winder shaft bearings and steam engine slides. From the 1950s iron castings were superseded by welded steel fabrications. Headgear

49 Fabricating a modern winder drum.

pulleys employed a bought-out cast steel boss onto which were welded angle section steel spokes and a rolled steel rim which was fitted with replaceable friction inserts to form the rope groove.

Two major winder projects involved the complete supply of winders and surface equipment. These were for Yorkshire Main colliery in 1905 and for the new Rothes colliery in 1946–56.

In the late 1960s Markham developed a medium pressure hydraulic winder brake. Hitherto the early Markham brakes were of the dead weight pneumatic and low-pressure hydraulic types. Latterly spring applied medium pressure hydraulic brakes were bought out as complete units from hydraulic brake specialists such as Blacks. The objective of the Markham brake development was to provide greater deceleration sensitivity, particularly when man riding, and improved safety. The brakes were spring applied and hydraulically released and had a redundant line of action from the spring to the brake post to overcome the danger of single line component failure. A test and demonstration rig was built with which Markham were able to convince the National Coal Board of the effectiveness and safety of the brake. Events such as the Markham colliery winder disaster, which resulted from a winder brake single line component failure, enforced a review of all winder brakes in use within the NCB. Mike Bennett, technical director at Markham until 1970 and later a consulting engineer, was retained by the NCB to review all winder brake installations and to recommend improvements where necessary to ensure compliance with essential safety requirements.

Many winder brake installations had to be replaced and Markham designed and supplied brake systems of both the calliper and disc type.

Markham was also entrusted with replacing twelve mine winder brakes in the Zambian Copper Belt.

Winder drum design was changing from cast iron to lighter fabricated steel construction; cracks developed emanating from fillet welds in the early fabricated designs, which tended to follow the geometry of the cast iron drum. Markham design department led by Mike Bennett, in conjunction with the British Welding Research Association and the Aeronautical Research Establishment at Farnborough analysed the problems and using the Sheffield Polytechnic mainframe computer developed a light and flexible drum which eliminated the cracking problems. This design method was used for all future winder drums.

Tunnelling machinery

The first record of orders for tunnelling machinery dates back to 1889 when eight shields for J.W. Williams were ordered, presumably from Olivers.

Since that date over 450 tunnelling machines (TBMs) and shields have been

50 A 10 m. diameter TBM built in 1988 to the design of Robbins (USA) for the Manapouri hydro-electric scheme, New Zealand.

built for such prestigious projects as: the metro rail tunnels for London, Paris, Moscow and Barcelona; the Post Office's Mount Pleasant railway under London; the Thames crossings at Rotherhithe and Dartford, which required two tunnels; the Mersey tunnel from Liverpool to Birkenhead; the Channel Tunnel, with the provision of two TBMs for the UK seaward rail tunnels; and the Cairo Waste Water project, for which three slurry TBMs were supplied in collaboration with the Okumura Corporation of Osaka, Japan.

The Okumura Corporation also licensed Markham to manufacture their remotely operated mini TBMs in the range of 600 mm to 1200 mm diameter. Control of tunnelling was from a specially equipped cabin on the surface. Using this technology a joint venture for mini tunnelling was established with Miller Construction, who were prominent civil engineering contractors specialising in tunnelling.

In 1987 a joint company was formed with the Robbins Company of Seattle called Robbins Markham JV, to tender for the Channel Tunnel rail tunnel TBMs. Robbins were the world's leading designers of hard rock TBMs. All four machines required on the UK side were tendered for and an order for the two seaward machines was received, James Howden of Glasgow securing the order for the two landward TBMs.

Following the Channel Tunnel contract a number of other collaborations were entered into. Markham manufactured a number of hard rock TBMs to Robbins design, two machines for the Lesotho Highlands Water Scheme, a 10m diameter machine for Manapouri in New Zealand and TBMs for the USA and Turkey.

Subsequently a licence arrangement was agreed with Kawasaki of Japan for Markham to manufacture machines to its design. The first machine built under this arrangement was a 5.85 m. diameter TBM for a tunnel for the Docklands Light railway.

The Channel Tunnel

Markham bid for the tunnelling shields and tunnelling machines for the channel tunnel project on four occasions. In 1929 and in 1973 bids were entered for pilot tunnel shields and machines but both projects were abortive.

In 1986 a bid was entered in conjunction with the Robbins Company of Seattle for the service tunnel machines for contractors Trans Manche Link (TML) but Howden of Glasgow were awarded the contract. In 1987 a bid, also in conjunction with Robbins, was entered for the running tunnel machines for the two landward and seaward drives.

The bid with Robbins was prepared on a joint venture basis with Robbins supplying the design of the cutting head and machine body, the supply of disc cutters and some other key components. Markham would provide the design for the back up system, which included the concrete segment handling and tunnel lining ring build system (the erector), the spoil conveyors and wagon filling system, ventilation and water pumping equipment and the associated electrics and control and guidance system. Markham would manufacture, assemble, works test, ship to site and reassemble the machines and back up systems.

The joint venture would be guaranteed by the parent companies. Each company would be paid its costs subject to detailed agreement and any resulting margin would be split 50–50.

In August 1987 the order was agreed with TML for the supply of the two seaward drive TBMs. The order value was £17.5 m. and the delivery period was to be 18 months for the first machine and 21 months for the second. Howden were awarded the order for the two landward drive machines.

One significant advantage of the joint venture was that the design content of the contract could be shared between the two design offices, making the required delivery time more achievable. The back-up system design was

51 A Francis pump storage turbine built by Markham for Foyers at Loch Ness.

subcontracted by Markham to consulting engineers Bennett Associates of Whiston, Rotherham, managed by Mike Bennett, the former technical director of Markham. Mutually compatible CAD software was used by Robbins and Bennett Associates, which resulted in a seamless interface between tunnelling machine and back-up system design.

The two TBMs were 8.36 m. in diameter and the total length of the machine and its back-up system stretched for a distance of 230 m. along the tunnel. The weight of each machine was about 1,500 tonnes and delivery to site of each machine required 150 lorry loads. Both machines were delivered on time and each was reassembled in a previously prepared underground chamber in a period of three months.

Early tunnelling difficulties were caused by unexpectedly high water inflows over the first 3 km of tunnelling. This required speedy re-design, mainly carried out on site by the Bennett Associates team, followed by site modification of the front end of the back-up system. Despite this setback the tunnels were completed on time with record weekly rates of advance of 430m. being achieved. This is believed to be a world record at the time for this size of TBM. Markham supplied on-site maintenance throughout the three-year long drives.

The final total contract value for the two TBMs, which included site modifications, spares, maintenance support and price escalation, was £27m.

Water turbines

After signing an agreement with Boving & Co. in 1928 Markham manufactured water turbines of all types and sizes as well as large penstock valves to Boving design. The first turbines were delivered in 1929.

Almost 300 turbines units were constructed at the Markham works during a 60-year period, with a total capacity or output of over 11,000 MW (see Appendix 1). This is equivalent to almost one third of all the electricity used in the UK in the year 2000. Of this 3,000 MW was installed in the UK.

The types of turbine built were Francis, Kaplan, Pelton, Francis mini-turbines, propeller and bulb types, and pump storage turbines. The principal contract of the last type was for the Dinorwic pump storage scheme in Wales, 'the electric mountain', known as 'spinning reserve', which acts like a gigantic rechargeable electric battery. Six units were supplied, with a total output of 1,900 MW. Pump storage turbines were also supplied for Foyers hydroelectric power station on Loch Ness and for Cruachan power station, both in Scotland, for Porabka-Zar in Poland, and for Villarino in Spain.

Major overseas hydroelectric projects where Markham-built turbines were supplied included Owen Falls in Uganda, Murray River in Australia, the Kariba dam in Zambia, El Chocon in Argentina, Planicie Banderita in Brazil

52 A 10.7 m. diameter Butterfly valve manufactured for the USA.

and Velle, Castrello and Friera in Spain.

The Boving agreement also covered the supply of valves, ships' thruster propellers and water control gates. Boving were a UK subsidiary of KMW who in turn were a member of the Swedish Axel Johnson Group. They were purchased by the Norwegian Kvaerner Group and then sold to General Electric of the USA. The Boving agreement was very advantageous to Markham, though there were some drawbacks.

53 A range of turbines on the shop floor.

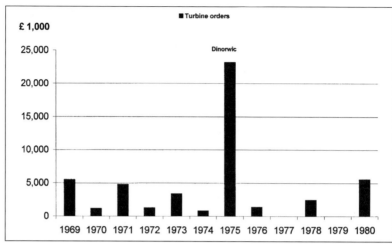

54 Water turbine order intake, 1969–80.

A spin-off from water turbine work was the development of the ability to weld stainless and high alloy steels and stainless clad mild steel plate, often of significant thickness. This enabled Markham to attract specialised subcontract work.

Water turbines accounted for around 30 per cent of turnover in the post-1960 period (see Appendix 7).

R.J. Barclay commented that water turbine business was Old Testament biblical in its style: seven good years followed by seven lean years. This would have related to the 1940s and 1950s. The table above seems to confirm the seven-year cycle. He also suggested that the water turbine business should not exceed a certain proportion of the company's order book, since otherwise management of the company resources and the servicing of other customers would become unduly difficult.

The nature of a water turbine order suited the Markham manufacturing profile quite well, particularly because during the period of over sixty years of the Boving agreement machine tools and skills had been adapted to such work. The advantages of the Boving water turbine business to Markham were: machining of turbine runners followed by heavy precision fitting and assembly provided work for all areas of the works; there was no design involvement with its attendant risk; there was multi-unit supply (although not more than six) and relatively long delivery periods, combined with a good spread over the manufacturing facilities, minimal contractual liabilities, and acceptable payment terms; in addition the stable nature of the customer enabled the development of specialised plant and skills to be evolved, particularly for quality assurance, the purchase of large steel castings, and specialised fabrication techniques.

There were also disadvantages. Water turbines assumed a superior position in the order book pecking order because of Boving's favoured customer position and their profitability, usually 30 per cent or more. Other customers often detected that they merited only second-class service and became frustrated by extended delivery times. Water turbine work, because of its particular suitability to the Markham plant and skills, would always be kept 'in house' while other work would be subcontracted if it clashed with water turbine manufacture, often with inferior or expensive results. Investment in plant, particularly heavy machines, was made with water turbines particularly in mind. This distorted plant availability for other work which could have been made more efficiently had plant been of a type more suited to general work been installed. Generally the large contract size of water turbine jobs gave rise to problems in providing continuous shop loading. When a large project was finished there was often a long gap before another turbine contract came into the workshops and often at a date which could not be forecast. This made the job of the sales department very onerous. Lastly, there was usually only a nominal down payment with no progress payments. Turnover, however, was taken as each unit of the turbine contract was shipped.

55 Managing director George Hand, accompanied by Chris Walters and Ian Williams, with the mayor of Chesterfield, Mrs A. Cowlishaw, and the town clerk, R.A. Kennedy, on a visit to Broad Oaks on 16 February 1967.

Castmaster

High pressure die-casting machines are used for repetition die-casting of aluminium, zinc, brass and lead components.

A licence was obtained from Cravens Machines, a sister company (later Bone Craven), who had a licence from HPM in Mount Gilead (Ohio) to sell and manufacture a range of plastics injection moulding and Castmaster metal die-casting machines in the UK. Cravens had found that involvement with die-casting interfered with their business in plastics machinery and they passed their die-casting interests over to Markham. The Castmaster design was very robust, well proven, and easy to maintain, but it was conservative. Markham produced a range of machines to two designs. The older type offered clamping forces of 100, 250, 500 or 800 tonnes, the newer one 400 or 600 tonnes.

The overall loss over the thirteen years of the operation was £139,000, or 3.1 per cent on sales of £4.49m. This begs the question of why it was allowed to continue for so long other than to keep people in employment. It allowed building for stock at times when the works were under-utilised, and it used the new numerically controlled machines which, having higher hourly rates, reduced under-recovery of the overhead. This factor of course did not show up in the profit and loss accounts.

56 A 500-ton Castmaster die-casting machine.

Die-casting machinery business financial summary

Year ending	Sales (£'000)	Profit/(loss) (£'000)
1969	27	(38)
1970	231	(43)
1971	199	(49)
1972	174	(4)
1973	266	(34)
1974	380	5
1975	232	(8)
1976	208	38
1977	466	(4)
1978	510	(38)
1979	1,041	69
1980	519	(31)
1981	236	(2)

Die-casting machines were always subject to strong competition from European suppliers. Triulzi, Italpresse and Idra of Italy, Bühler of Switzerland and Wotan of Germany all offered generally more sophisticated machines together with a very flexible pricing policy. Markham found that to compete they had to specialise and customise machines, which required in-house design work in order to achieve any market at all. In particular, custom-designed automated hot chamber machines were required for the production of battery grids made of lead-antimony alloys.

Principal customers for aluminium die-casting machines were Joseph Lucas of Birmingham and Singer of Glasgow, with exports going to South Korea, South Africa and Pakistan. Battery grid die-casting machines were sold to Oldham Batteries and to Chloride Industrial Batteries Ltd in the UK and overseas to Brazil, France and China.

Die-casting machines lent themselves to batch production, which in turn meant a level of stock higher than Markham was used to. Markham's inflexible overhead rates were geared to water turbine production rather than to batch production of small light machines, which had an appreciable hydraulic and electrical content. This, together with a declining market, killed the product. The die-casting business did however give Markham fitters valuable experience in high-pressure hydraulics, which was advantageous in the forthcoming anode press and TBM projects.

The decline of the die-casting industry in the UK during the mid 1980s led to a large number of secondhand machines coming onto the market and the disposal of the Markham die-casting business to Michael Lloyd, who operated a reconditioning and spares business for Castmaster machinery owners.

Coating and laminating

The coating and laminating business essentially comprised the provision to sister company Bone Craven (later Bone Markham) of a much-needed skilled manufacturing facility geared to custom-built one-off production.

The coating and laminating business operated under a licence from Egan of the USA arranged with Craven's sister company Bone Brothers of Alperton. This company had been purchased by John Brown and incorporated into the John Brown–Cravens plastics business.

Machinery supplied via Bone Craven's designs included extrusion coating lines, both single and tandem, for applying a polyethylene web to a variety of substrates; phenolic treatment lines for the manufacture of insulating materials such as TUFNOL; dip waxers for bread wrapping paper; reverse roll coating lines for the application of wet coatings; laminating lines for laminating paper with plastic, paper with foil, plastic with foil and foil or plastic with adhesive; and drying ovens for wet coated material.

Cravens supplied the extruders from their Sheffield works and provided some specialist machinery such as thickness gauges and ovens.

From 1967 to the early 1980s Markham built approximately one hundred coating lines of various types, starting with three extrusion coating lines for the USSR which were completed on time and passed the works tests without a hitch. A description of the Russian machines and their construction was published by Ken Wort and included in *Broad Oaks*, the company's house magazine: 'The machine supplied was designed to coat a 'web' of cellulose film with 0.001 to 0.004 inch thickness of Polyethylene, but paper, aluminium foil, cloth and other types of packaging film can also be coated. It operated at a web speed of 30 to 350 ft/min. and from 70 to 1,500 lb/hr of Polyethylene'.

A light-hearted complementary article written by Richard Jones of Bone Brothers gave Markham employees and families an insight into the paper converting industry.

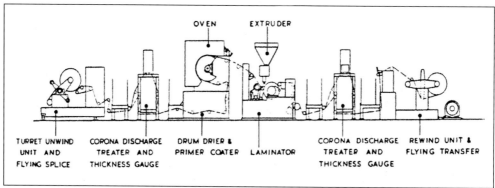

57 A 60-inch wide film extrusion coating line made for the USSR.

Coating and laminating business summary

Year ending	Sales (£'000)	Profit/(loss) (£'000)
1970	917	10
1971	1921	131
1972	373	(18)
1973	890	24
1974	1108	81
1975	1029	19
1976	1290	18
1977	492	(24)
1978	451	(18)
1979	2518	362
1980	523	102
1981	1153	(58)

The business was administered by a joint Bone-Markham board and the range of machines built included wallpaper coating lines, photographic paper

58 Part of the phenolic treatment line made for BXL, showing the left-hand end of the machine which appears in the diagram opposite.

coaters for Kodak, waxers for bread wrapping, packaging material base coaters and floor covering material coaters. Customers included Sanderson, ICI, British Sisalkraft and St Regis Bates of New Zealand. Due to a congenial collaboration of individuals the association was both profitable and pleasant with Bill Taylor, Keith Johnston and David Grant at the top and Richard Jones of Bone Brothers and Ken Wort of Markham at management level. Barry Stevens of Markham and Eric Esgate of Bone Brothers led the design and production engineering.

The business was ultimately transferred to Bone Cravens newly acquired yet old-established factory of Daniels of Stroud.

The overall profit on the operation was £629,000, or 5 per cent on sales of £12.656m. (see table on p. 77). This was appreciably better than the die-casting business and was partly due to the fact that there was no Markham design content. Markham was not responsible for sales and virtually no level of stock was required.

Stowing machinery

Markham stowing equipment was developed from the late 1940s to pack waste material in mines at up to 75 per cent of the virgin ground density in areas from which coal had been extracted. Waste from the mining operation was used as the filler material, which reduced the quantity that had to be taken to the surface. In the case of full face stowing however, additional debris was recirculated from surface spoil heaps. The main purposes of stowing were to reduce subsidence of the ground surface, especially in sensitive areas such as beneath churches, sewage works, town centres etc., and to pack the sides of roadways to protect and consolidate them and to channel the flow of ventilation air.

Stowing was carried out using either high- or low-pressure air. High-pressure air at 100 psi was piped from surface compressors and Markham developed automatic flow control valves to regulate and conserve the air entering the stower. Markham also pioneered the use of low-pressure air using positive Roots type displacement blowers operating at up to 10 psi. The blowers were also used in series to generate up to 25 psi pressure.

The stowing machines were designed for extremely heavy duty, and a range of machines with a rotor with shaped pockets to introduce the waste material into the air stream was developed. Special low-profile crushers were designed to feed suitably sized material into the stowing machines. Internally hardened steel pipelines with special wear resistant bends and diverter valves were used. These systems became very popular with the NCB and were supplied extensively to the coal industry. Over 400 units were sold until the late 1960s when over a hundred old mines, many of which relied on stowing

59 The pneumatic conveying test-rig.

for their existence, were closed. This, together with the introduction of self-advancing face chocks used to keep pace with the rapid excavation of both advance and retreat faces, resulted in the demise of stowing in UK coalmines. A maintenance, servicing and rebuild service had been offered and had been very busy and profitable during the 20-year period of stowing's heyday.

From the 1960s and until about 1990 low-pressure pneumatic transportation was increasingly used for conveying a variety of materials. In 1965 a test rig, designed in the drawing office under Mike Bennett's guidance, was built at Markham to investigate the parameters governing pneumatic conveying. The rig was built outside adjacent to the end wall of the boiler shop. Many different materials were evaluated and formulae developed to predict their conveying performance over varying distance and height. The rig was designed to operate in the continuous dilute phase rather than as a high-pressure dense phase batch system.

Prior to this and using only one material, mine waste, it had been sufficient to rely upon experience gained from trial and error. It proved possible in the test rig to convey successfully much higher density materials than mine waste.

For example, a complete system was developed for conveying pulverised fly ash from power station precipitator hoppers to storage hoppers and a trial system was installed at Willington power station. Handling the very fine

60 A combination of stower, crusher and low-pressure air blower.

powdered abrasive fly ash required a special approach to bearing design and a system of sealing the bearing housing using pressurised air was successfully developed. After ironing out teething problems a complete handling plant comprising 16 machines was installed at Ratcliffe power station in 1967 and successfully operated until 1989.

A system was also developed to handle and convey a dry lean mix concrete which could, for instance, be used to pack around large diameter concrete pipes as added protection and support when laid in trenches. Inherent moisture in the aggregate and natural ground water was generally sufficient to set the concrete. If required water could be introduced close to the discharge end of the conveying pipeline. The system was licensed to Blastmixer Ltd of Huddersfield.

In deep coal mining spillage accumulates in the sump of skip hoisting shafts and Markham stowing machines were used to convey spillage pneumatically at a rate of 20 tons per hour by pipeline from the sump to the skip measuring pockets with vertical lifts of between 18 and 152 meters.

Two systems were installed at Whitwell lime works to convey pneumatically lime dust from precipitator hoppers to storage bunkers.

Crushed ice is used on board trawlers to cover fish at sea as boxes of fish are filled and stacked in racks below deck. This is a very labour intensive job and difficult in a rough sea. A system was developed for the White Fish Authority at Hull to both crush the ice and convey it via a flexible pipe so that it could be sprayed on to the fish boxes in the hold.

A system was installed in one of ICI's salt mines in Cheshire to supplement the skip hoisting capacity. Use was made of an existing 200 mm diameter pipeline in the shaft to convey minus 100 mm size rock salt vertically at the rate of about 75 tonnes per hour.

A stowing installation was supplied to the new potash mines at Boulby in Northumberland.

Vertical transportation of coal up mine shafts was developed to supplement winder capacity. Systems were supplied to the Miskolc coalmine in northern Hungary where 100 tonnes of coal per hour was transported 366m vertically in a 500 mm diameter pipe.

Stowers for transporting and consolidating excavated rock were supplied to the San Telmo mercury mines in Spain.

Product development

After the Second World War Markham sought to improve their sales base by adding new product ranges, preferably within industries with which they were familiar.

Stowing machinery was introduced into the coal mines based upon low-pressure high-volume air moving heavy material at high speed through pipelines. The conveyed material was used to replace underground excavated material with waste products at up to 90 per cent of the original ground density.

The original design was seemingly taken from the Beien (Czechoslovak) machine. Ultimately, a range of equipment was developed, including wear resistant pipes and bends, Roots type blowers in conjunction with Holmes of Huddersfield, valves, stowers and crushers. The range of equipment was marketed in a number of combinations.

Other than for pneumatic conveying, Markham did not have a consistent and budgeted approach to product development, as was probably the case in Charles Markham's day. A number of ad hoc attempts were made to introduce new products, but a narrow-minded skinflint approach meant that the first installation had to pay for itself or was considered to be a failure! It was therefore no surprise that virtually all attempts were a failure! A development committee chaired by Sir Eric Mensforth was established and a number of projects were examined:

Techite pipe. This was a plastic pipe for gas pipelines and for other

61 The VS 45 variable speed wind turbine.

services. It was abandoned since Markham did not have a sales network which could compete with similar products.

Road stone crusher. This was a high specification breaker, which Bardon Hill Quarries were looking to develop, utilising Firth Brown tool's tungsten carbide for the flail blades. The project was abandoned when Ken Wort discovered that Krupp already had such a product established on the market.

Packaging machine. This was developed with an American inventor to compete with Tetrapack but was abandoned after making much progress due to the intransigence of the inventor.

After the development committee was terminated a number of developments were attempted, albeit with caution. These were:

Mine winder brakes. A medium-pressure hydraulically applied calliper brake system was designed in the drawing office. Several systems were installed in local NCB mines, latterly using disc pads. Unfortunately the market declined drastically as mines closed.

Mine haulages. This was a modern version of the very successful Markham range of haulages but utilising hydraulic power. The product was an initial success but again the market declined drastically as mines closed.

Roadway supports. Two types of moveable mine roadway supports were developed, self-advancing and externally moved. Though both were successful it was too late: as with the previous two developments we missed the boat!

Wave energy. Cooperation with Professor Stephen Salter produced outline designs for the 'nodding duck' but the Department of Trade and Industry did not give it financial backing.

Wind turbines. A variable speed turbine VS 45 was built but the UK market proved to be fickle and larger power foreign turbines overtook it.

Die-casting. This was the only successful product, although overall it lost money. Latterly an integrated system was developed for battery grid production. Six systems were sold but the market was limited.

General engineering after 1958

This important contribution to the Markham order book was necessary in order to fill in the gaps in works capacity not taken up by its principal products, water turbines, tunnelling machinery and mining equipment.

The art of determining and securing such work lay in the appreciation of the type of work which Markham could undertake at profitable prices and realistic delivery, coupled with an ongoing knowledge of the amount and type of works capacity that was likely to be available. This required an active understanding of what the market could offer both in the short and medium term over a range of possibilities as wide as could be envisaged. This also required lateral thinking in terms of subcontracting in order to achieve required deliveries and pricing requirements, particularly when an order for

62 Advanceable roadway supports.

a water turbine or winder unexpectedly arrived 'out of the blue'. It was necessary to look worldwide for suitable work.

Many of Markham's contracts involved site installation and Jack Brown was the manager of the outside erection department, which had its own well-equipped cabins.

General engineering work usually needed to account for around 25 to 30 per cent of the annual turnover.

Quality assurance

The inspection department, later to be known as the quality assurance (QA) department, was accorded a primary and independent role in the Markham manufacturing system from the very early days.

Quality control was exercised over bought-in materials and components. Rigid inspection of parts and assemblies made in the workshops was essential for the smooth and timely flow of manufacture, as well as for the preservation of product integrity.

Over the years developments in national and international QA techniques were quickly assimilated into the Markham regime and the QA manager reported directly to the managing director. Frank Cherry ran the department between 1965 and 1985.

Markham QA was very comprehensive and included:

Dimensional inspection. Slip gauges, vernier and micrometer equipment used by operatives for measurement was regularly calibrated using a Societe Genevoise measuring comparator housed in its own temperature controlled room.

Material checking. Verification against externally supplied test certificates.

Mechanical. Izod impact and Denison tensile testing machines were used, with test specimens checked with an Ultraphot microscope.

Non-destructive testing. A separate radiography building, designed in-house, was built to take work pieces as large as 8m × 6m × 3m. A portable gamma source was also stored in the facility. Ultrasonic testing was also widely used for checking welds.

Paper trail. Rigorous control of test certificates was maintaned for all purchased materials.

Authentication. Great care was taken to assemble and prepare QA documentation to guarantee and authenticate material quality and dimensional veracity.

Liaison with customer's inspectors. Customers and national inspection authorities were frequently in the works. Liaison and assistance was provided without compromising outside the inspector's independence.

Finishing off and painting

The Markham ethos had for many years been 'make it so that it works and lasts for 20 years at least'. Once a component or assembly had reached this stage the Markham worker's interest faded, thinking that finishing off and painting were unnecessary, effete and a diversion from getting on with the next job. Thus weld spatter, extraneous and internal swarf, and indifferent paintwork tended to characterise Markham's products in the years immediately after the Second World War.

63 Denis Crich using the Société Genèvoise comparator.

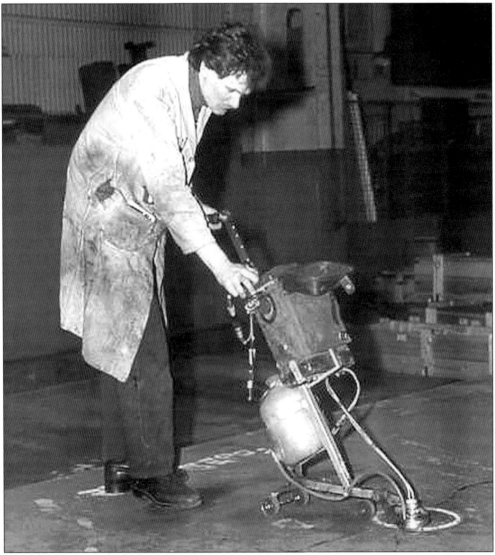

64 Ultrasonic testing of a plate.

Prior to this there was the case of the bridge girders supplied to China in the 1930s, coated with the infamous 'never dry' black paint, probably bitumen based. They were wet on leaving the works and still wet when they arrived in China—they may even still be wet!

An expensive example of Markham indifference to finishing was the contract to supply coating line equipment to ICI in the late 1970s. The contract included a detailed and elaborate painting specification, which required as the last stage a 'duster proof' finish which meant that a lamb's wool duster passed over the surface of the machine would not result in any snags to the duster or duster particles adhering to the painted surface. Compliance with the painting specification undoubtedly cost more than the bought-in materials and parts for the construction of the equipment and resulted in a hefty loss!

Other sorry examples were the pulverising mills built for a South Korean power station, where variations in temperature during painting due to opening and closing the large erecting shop doors resulted in sheets of finished paint falling off the mill bodies when they were moved. This same phenomenon caused considerable embarrassment to Ken Wort in China when Chinese engineers were able to peel paint layers off the clamp assembly of a die-casting machine.

Transport

Transportation of large and heavy components from the works in the centre of England to other UK destinations and to the docks has called for considerable expertise in the design of the product so that it had suitable joints to enable it to be split into transportable sizes. Loading and securing the load to a suitable vehicle and collaborating with transport contractors and police is important.

Since oversize loads can cause traffic bottlenecks, prescribed routes have to be agreed and authorised, often requiring police escort and sometimes

65 An example of a very large load moved by road from Broad Oaks.

assistance to pass under power cables and telephone lines.

Shipment of the Channel Tunnel TBMs, each weighing 1,500 tonnes when assembled, required 150 loads for each machine to be taken down to site near Folkestone.

There were a few transport disasters. A winding drum left its transport vehicle in the mid 1960s and ploughed through some cars in the forecourt of Pilkington Motors in Chesterfield, and a cement kiln section became wedged under the railway bridge near the works. Generally, however, transport was managed skilfully and economically.

Trading overseas

Africa

After the delivery of 31 winders to South Africa in the late 1920s and 1930s, Markham did no further winder business in Africa until the 1970s. Then contact was made with Blanes, an agent in South Africa, who operated a refurbishment operation with large machining capability, and orders for two winders, parts and spares were received in 1982.

In the Zambian copper belt the effect of the British Coal review of winder brake design generated a demand for replacement brake engines throughout the ZCCM mines. Gordon Paterson, Markham's agent in Zambia, was well connected and Markham supplied new brake systems to 12 of the ZCCM winders through his efforts.

The State Gold Mines in Ghana had to replace old winders at all their mines and it was decided that Markham would tender for them as a subcontractor to NEI. Orders for nine winders resulted in 1990. Subsequently a refurbishment order for a winder for Ashanti was received in 1996.

In the 1960s Sir Eric Mensforth instigated meetings of John Brown subsidiary company technical directors. Resulting from this was collaboration with Wickman South Africa to try to develop a machine to cut selectively the very narrow band of gold, the reef, which is only about 1 cm thick, embedded in the granite mass. Mike Bennett visited South Africa on two occasions to explore the possibilities with Johan Raal, Wickman's South African resident engineer. The idea was to use a vertical shaft-mounted flail fitted with hinged Wickman tungsten carbide clad blades. Had such a machine been successful it would literally have led to a pot of gold. Unfortunately the internal compressive stress in the rock at great depth, several thousands of feet, was so high that even at a high speed of rotation the blades were 'nipped' in the rock. The only good thing was a weekend in the Kruger national park!

Bahrain

In the late 1960s and early 1970s a rash of aluminium smelters were under construction, three in the UK, one near Fort William, one in Anglesey and one at Lynemouth, together with a few around the world, including Iran and Bahrain.

The Bahrain smelter was built to cushion the Bahrain economy in the post oil period. Aluminium smelters are heavy users of electrical power. The UK smelters were each linked to a specific power source, Fort William to hydropower, Anglesey to the Wylfa nuclear power station, and Lynemouth to its own custom-built coal-fired power station, which was built by Foster Wheeler John Brown Boilers and incorporating Markham-built coal pulverising mills. The Bahrain smelter drew its power from Kuff gas from depleted oil wells driving John Brown Engineering-built and GE-designed gas turbines. The smelter was financed from British loans guaranteed by the Export Credit Guarantee Department, with a requirement that a large and specified proportion of the equipment should be of British supply. Most of the plant involved in an aluminium smelter is lighter than was ideal for Markham manufacture but Markham were asked via the John Brown connection to look at the hydraulic press equipment required for the production of the carbon anodes used in the electrolysis process which converts alumina into aluminium metal.

Anodes are produced in the 'paste' plant where the carbon paste material is produced to a prescribed recipe from crushed petroleum coke and pitch, carefully blended, and then pressed into a rectangular block form by a hydraulic press or vibrator.

The paste plant consultant for the Bahrain smelter was Peter Fischer, a Swiss engineer, and he had specified a 2,500-tonne Swiss-designed press from Von Roll of Klus, Switzerland for the anode production. Von Roll had gained the impression that they were to supply and build the press and at a strained meeting in Klus, Von Roll reluctantly agreed to consider an arrangement with Markham as manufacturer. A visit from Von Roll's technical director to Markham went well: he saw Castmaster machines in production and expressed his satisfaction with Markham's production capability. The next meeting was in Klus and Von Roll insisted on supplying the press mould and hydraulics, which were to be from Towler of Leeds but with Von Roll pumps. As an afterthought it was suggested that Markham employ a Von Roll engineer for the duration of the project as this would help him to perfect his English.

As it turned out the engineer, Peter Spiegel, became a valued member of the drawing office, a member of Chesterfield Male Voice choir and he and his wife have become firm friends of the Wort family.

After a very cautious beginning the association with Von Roll worked very well, although two unusual problems had to be overcome. Markham terms of payment to Von Roll were thought to breach the strict exchange control regulations in force in 1970 and Ken Wort had to pay his one and only visit to the Bank of England to justify the terms. His explanation was accepted with a caveat of 'don't do it again'. The second problem occurred with commissioning the press in Bahrain. Peter Spiegel was Markham's commissioning engineer and the commissioning period became substantially over-extended through difficulties with the rest of the plant. Frau Spiegel, newly wed, and a very forthright lady, confronted Von Roll and insisted that she be reunited with her husband in Bahrain, usually unheard of in engineering but you didn't argue with Lydia Spiegel when she was sure she was in the right.

A second press was ordered to provide strategic back-up in 1973.

The Markham team, Jack Brown, Walt Edson, Chris Peacock, Harry Lacy and Alan Rhodes, performed most creditably in one of the hottest climates in the world.

In 1982 Markham won a contract to design and supply a slab conveyor for the ALBA aluminium smelter casting house. The design was sublet to Mike Bennett's company Skeltonhall and the conveyor installation and commissioning overseen by John Blankley.

China

In the 1930s Markham had supplied bridge girders to China, painted with Markham black 'never dry' paint. In the 1950s a stowing machine assembly was supplied.

In the 1970s the John Brown group decided to concentrate their export attention on China and participated in a British commercial exhibition in Beijing in 1975. Markham was invited to exhibit and they showed mine winder and tunnelling machine photographs and a battery grid casting produced by a Castmaster die-casting machine. Boving were exhibiting separately.

Great interest was shown in the battery grid casting and the Chinese followed up the exhibition by asking for a quotation for a battery grid die-casting machine assembly.

The quotation was to be submitted to the China State Shipbuilding Corporation on behalf of the Zibo Battery Company, a medium-sized battery producer in Zibo City in Shandong province about 300 miles south of Beijing. After a series of visits and discussions a contract was agreed and a 600-ton Castmaster battery grid machine assembly was delivered. We understood that the battery grids were for railway and lighting standby use but these particular grids are also used in submarine batteries!

Germany

In the early 1960s Markham became involved in the manufacture of steelworks plant when the introduction of universal beam sections into steel building construction generated a demand for new rolling mill equipment in the UK. Boris Ryman, agent for DEMAG of Duisburg in Germany, had secured orders for two universal beam mills, one for South Durham Steel & Iron Co. and one for Shelton Iron & Steel, and was looking for British manufacture for the run out tables and transfer equipment. A manufacturing agreement was made with John Brown SEND Ltd and the manufacture of over 600 tonnes of steelworks plant for each mill was ordered from Markham.

In the late 1960s the development of continuous casting machinery was well advanced in Germany and, with the Ryman agreement now expired, DEMAG were again looking for British manufacture to enable them to supply machines to British steelworks. The first contract received by DEMAG was for the Anchor development at the British Steel Corporation works in Scunthorpe and Markham received an order from DEMAG for the supply of run out tables, billet stops, slab yard and transfer cars, amounting to about 1,000 tonnes of plant together with installation.

Subsequently orders were received for a billet caster for Manchester Steel and a bloom caster for Round Oak steelworks, Brierley Hill.

Securing these orders involved considerable sales effort in Germany and Mike Bennett supplied staunch and able support to Ken Wort. In their free time one evening in a bar in Duisburg Mike was so tired that he nodded off leaning on the bar over his glass of wine and cut his eyebrow, blood pouring everywhere. Ken thought that they would be thrown out but no, charming and scantily clad waitresses bore Mike to the powder room and dressed his wound—that's what he said anyway. A team of Davy United men were also in the bar and were very jealous.

Low British labour rates and exchange control restrictions helped to make Markham supply attractive to German companies throughout the 1960s and 1970s and Markham were successful in securing further work from DEMAG, together with orders from Krupp of Rheinhausen and Krupp of Wilhelmshaven as well as from Klockner Humbolt Deutz.

Eastern Europe

In the early 1970s exporting to the Eastern European countries was encouraged by the Government and the banks, with favourable Export Credit Guarantee Department-backed loans made available to preferred countries.

Export houses sought to put together deals which would qualify for loans and in the die-casting industry Morganite International, of the Morgan

Crucible Group, was prominent.

Markham, being the leading UK maker of high-pressure die-casting machines, was invited to participate in bids for complete factories for making Westinghouse motorcar brake components for Poland and carburettor parts for Romania. The bids involved several UK companies and incorporated both low- and high-pressure die-casting machines, trimming presses, furnaces, and deburring and polishing machines ,with Morganite International dealing with coordination, finance, ECGD, counter trade and local sales representation.

Neither bid was successful since other West European countries submitted more attractive bids.

Morganite International was ultimately disbanded and two of its Eastern European agents, Stephen Somogyi of Hungary and Vladislav Semenovic of Yugoslavia, were retained by Markham for sales work in Eastern Europe.

Subsequently Stephen Somogyi introduced an enquiry for shaft sinking equipment for Ostrava in Czechoslovakia and Vlad Semenovic an enquiry for a tunnelling machine for a hydroelectric project at Zavoj, near Pirot in Serbia. Neither project was successfully concluded: the Czech project was lost on technical grounds to an American shaft borer and the Serbian job to a German company who were offering a refurbished machine at a much lower price than Markham could supply a new machine.

Mott MacDonald accompanied the Markham sales team on at least two occasions to Yugoslavia with a view to obtaining contracts for the design and supply of TBMs supply for proposed new metro schemes. Such work did not materialise.

In the early 1980s Markham were approached by Arcon, an American based agency in the USSR, to put forward a proposal for a tunnelling machine for the construction of a tunnel in Moscow in water-bearing soils for a district heating project. Over an eighteen-month period a number of visits were made to the USSR and various proposals put forward. The initial requirement was for a 5.15 m. diameter TBM but this was finally amended to 2.9m diameter. The Japanese, who had the distinct advantage of having a permanent representative in Moscow and who were able to offer a wide range of counter trade alternatives for payment, eventually won the contract.

Iceland

Markham received an enquiry from the Icelandic fabrication company Sindra Smidgeon of Rejkyavik for a bifurcation to be installed in a hydro-power pipeline on the Laxa river at Akureyri in northern Iceland. An agreement was made with Krupp Rheinhausen for access to their patented design, the order was received and the bifurcation supplied. Stan Ball went to Iceland to oversee the site welding.

Trade associations

Trade associations have played an important part in the work of engineering companies over the last 60 years or so and while today they are regarded as an obstruction to free trade and competition, they have been valuable in furthering desirable collaboration. This was particularly necessary during the war years when the acquisition of men and materials and sub-contract capacity was both essential and difficult. After the war, trade associations were particularly helpful when dealing with nationalised industries with their monolithic control over a section of business. Other benefits included access to specialised legal departments and to model forms of contract conditions, and the opportunity to participate in exhibitions organised or sponsored by trade associations and in overseas trade missions.

Markham was a member of the Winding Engine Manufacturers Association, the Steel Works Plant Makers Association, the Die Casting Society, the Forge-masters Association, the Engineering Employers Federation, and the British Electrical and Associated Manufacturers Association.

Competitors

Good competitors are essential to keep an engineering company on its toes.

The Boving agreement effectively kept competition one step removed but Boving left Markham in no doubt about their need to be competitive. In the winder business long-term UK competitors were M.B. Wild of Birmingham, GEC Erith, and Robeys of Lincoln, as well as GHH and DEMAG of Germany.

Most tunnelling machinery competition other than Howden of Glasgow in later years came from overseas such as Herrenknecht and Wirth of Germany, Kawasaki, Mitsubishi and Hitachi of Japan, Lovat of Canada and latterly Babcock Fives Lille and Framatome of France. Howden entered the business in 1980 as a diversification from their industrial fan business and it was Howden who built the other UK channel tunnel TBMs. The competition was fierce and Markham found it necessary to seek alliances with Robbins and with Kawaski in the later years.

Jimmy Simpson, sales director of Newton Chambers, and Ken Wort used to meet once a quarter to exchange information and to commiserate over a pint or two on their respective lots. Newton Chambers were very good and competitive at making large rectangular things but Jimmy's managing director was always pushing him to get orders for cylindrical work such as mine winders, which Jimmy knew would be disastrous. Markham of course excelled in the manufacture of cylindrical things but was seldom able to compete for rectangular work, which the sales department were urged to obtain!

Sister companies

The position of Markham vis à vis its sister companies varied with the nature of the group to which it belonged at the time.

Markham was the only specialist engineering company in the Staveley coal, iron and chemicals group and so it was favoured with much in-house business. This helped in export work as a source for technical reference and process know-how.

The transfer to the John Brown Group took place in 1937 and group involvement was minimal so far as Markham was concerned during the war. Afterwards a substantial part of John Brown's assets were nationalised. At this time Markham was heavily involved in work to rebuild the country's industry. John Brown's policy was for each operating unit to perform as a separate company and be individually accountable though paying substantial management fees to the group. Markham fitted well into the John Brown development plans, particularly with John Brown SEND and the nuclear venture, and also with Foster Wheeler John Brown Boilers and PHI Engineering who required pulverising mill manufacture for their power station programmes and cement plant business.

In the late 1960s a mutually satisfactory collaboration was arranged between Cravens, i.e. Cravens Machines and Bone Brothers, and Markham to build Bone Brothers converting machinery at Markham and for Markham to take over the manufacture of the HPM licensed Cast Master die-casting machinery.

The Trafalgar House takeover of John Brown introduced two new sister companies, Cementation and Cleveland Bridge, who had interests in mining, tunnelling and structural engineering. The Davy Group of Sheffield, renamed Davy Metals, were a part of the group and would eventually absorb Markham following the Kvaerner takeover.

Markham's sister companies over the years can be summarised thus:

Staveley Coal & Iron Company

John Brown Group
  Constructors John Brown
    Eric Johnson Stubbs: North Sea gas conversions
    Automatic Control Engineering: electrical control systems
  John Brown SEND Ltd
  Wickman Group: automatic lathes
    Webster and Bennett: vertical lathes
    Laing: lathes
    Scrivener: centreless grinders
    Kitchen Walker: drills

Stirk: planers
Taylor and Challen: mechanical presses
PHI Engineering Ltd: pulverising mills
Craven Tasker: trailers.
Strick Containers
East Lancs. Coach Builders: buses
Merryweather: fire engines
Cravens Ltd: auto car parks
Cravens Machines: HPM licence; plastics injection moulding machines.
Bone Brothers: Egan licence; coating and converting machinery.
Tooling Products: dies for the plastics industry
John Brown Engineering: GE gas turbine licence
John Brown Clydebank
Bridges: electric hand tools
Foster Wheeler John Brown Boilers: Whitecrook Works; coal-fired power
station boiler plant
Solartron John Brown: automatic warehouses

Trafalgar House Group
Trafalgar House Construction
Cementation Group
Cleveland Bridge and Engineering
Cunard Group
Davy Metals
Trollop and Colls
Ritz Hotel
Ideal Homes

Kvaerner Group

The company at work

Reminiscences of Herbert Stone

Herbert Stone joined Markham in 1922 during the post-war depression when some of the workshops were down to three days a week. Here are some of his reminiscences.

'Outwardly the works did not change much in the next forty years or so. The previous forty years, however, had been years of regular growth to match the vast industrial expansion of the late Victorian and Edwardian period. The end of 1918 saw the completion of the last big extensions, the erecting and turbine shops. The "Turbine" was not water but an aspiration to steam turbines, which never materialised.'

Internally the changes in Herbert Stone's time were tremendous, the most marked being the vast improvement of working conditions. Having said that, in C.P. Markham's time things were better than in most comparable workplaces: as sole owner he cultivated a dedicated and highly skilled team

66 Herbert Stone (seated left) on his retirement, with Bill Taylor (standing) and R.J. Barclay.

and looked after them. Markham had a licensed canteen, and also a rest home at Holymoorside, paid for by CP, for men in need of recuperation after illness. When food prices immediately after the end of the First World War began to get out of hand, CP opened a shop in Hollis Lane and sold cut-price groceries.

What was to become the fitting shop was partly occupied by a range of Lancashire boilers and a tall brick-built chimney. These boilers fed a vertical steam engine in No. 9 bay of the machine shop which drove all the overhead shafting and was kept as a stand-by even after electric drive was fitted to most machines. When Mike Bennett joined Markham in 1958 line belts still operated in the small machine bay. In 1922 the six 10-ton capacity cranes were also driven by overhead shafting from endless belts running on guide pulleys for the length of the bays. The crane cross travel motion was also belt-driven via friction clutches.

Herbert Stone continues:

'The general impression of the machine shop was one of noise from the belt drives and gloom from the black unpainted machines and shop steelwork. There was a wide gangway with a rail track and the *Duchess of Sutherland* steam loco would puff its way up the machine shop filling the place with smoke and steam. In winter, coke braziers added their quota of dirt and smoke.

'Work was measured almost exclusively by inside and outside callipers together with ring and pin gauges. The skilled old-timer could nevertheless turn out work to a standard equal to anything that could be produced forty years later. Toleranced drawings were unheard of and so of course interchangeability could not apply. This did not matter since there was no mass production in those days at Markham and spares were made from site measurements.' This practice was still prevalent even in the early 1960s when Mike Bennett took over as chief engineer. He had a hard job introducing toleranced drawings and numerical grades of machine finish.

In 1922 the range of activities covered within the works was far wider than in the 1980s. In the first place the works was divided into two businesses, mechanical and structural engineering, each with its own drawing and estimating offices and departmental chiefs. The mechanical side covered the pattern shop, iron and brass foundries and even a short lived 'white elephant' steel foundry, forge and machine, fitting and erecting shops. The structural department manufactured parts for framed buildings, bridge girders, pithead gear and general plate work, all of which was riveted either by machine or pom-pom hammer.

Electric welding was in its infancy, carried out by one man working part-time in a corner behind screens and mainly covering up errors and omissions. Welding was considered to be an abomination by the visiting colliery engineers. This said, Markham were one of the first heavy engineering concerns to take up welding seriously in 1930.

67 The 1977 children's party in the works canteen.

There was of course the 'German' crane in the yard installed in 1904 towering 120 feet high, spanning an area of 50 by 100 yards, and in use for 45 years. It was a first class advertisement since it could be seen far and wide, and most clearly from the main railway line.

The garage was run as a separate business under a garage manager. Markham Garage was one of the first motor repair shops to be opened in Chesterfield and for some years held the Ford agency in the days when the famous Model T outsold all others. Henry Ford however decided that the British should drive on the right and only made left-hand drive cars; he also decreed that you could have any colour provided that it was black. This killed the Ford car in Britain for a time and made way for Austin and Morris. By 1922 the garage business was on its last legs, the Ford agency having been taken over in 1915 by the then small firm of Kennings.

Herbert Stone became works manager following Frank Williams in 1959 and retired in 1970.

Daily routine, social side and amenities

The works day shift started at 7.30 a.m. and staff at 8.30 a.m. Directors and departmental managers attended a morning meeting at 9 a.m. Shop floor lunch was from 12 to 1 and staff from 1 to 2 o'clock. There were separate dining arrangements and locations for shop floor workers, junior staff, senior staff, departmental managers and of course for the directors. Departmental managers and the directors took an afternoon tea break in the managers' mess at 4 p.m. This was said to be useful for communication (football) and for planning the following day! The works day shift ended at 4.30 and staff were free to go home at 5.00, though many did not do so.

There were a number of annual social events in the early 1960s when Mike Bennett first encountered Markham. These included a foremen's outing, a coach trip to somewhere of interest and dinner on the way back, for foremen and staff of equivalent rank or above, to which the directors and their wives were invited. The foremen's association was not confined to Markham and included men from two other local heavy engineering companies, Brian Donkin and the Chesterfield Tube Company. They had a monthly evening meeting, usually with an invited guest speaker.

The black-tie staff dinner dance, to which local dignitaries were invited, was held annually around Christmas time, usually at the Odeon (now the Winding Wheel). All staff and wives were invited and was very popular.

A children's Christmas party was held in the works canteen cum social club and there was an entertainer, Santa, and of course presents. The wives of senior staff were recruited to assist and supervise the proceedings. As far back

68 The works canteen, heavily disguised by Fretwell Downing of Sheffield, for a function in 1961 to mark the centenary of Oliver & Co.'s establishment.

69 A staff outing to Whitby. R.J. Barclay is standing on the extreme left; third from the right is Reg Dean.

as 1931 this was the same format and in that year 230 children attended.

The apprentices' open day consisted of a prize giving to which parents and relatives were invited and had the opportunity to inspect the apprentices' workplace and their handiwork. There were light refreshments and an opportunity to look round the works. A cup was presented to the craft apprentice of the year.

There were sports days with interdepartmental cricket and bowls matches. Markham also played bowls and tennis against Firth Brown Tools and Staveley. A singles golf competition was held at Matlock and the G.W. Hand Greensomes competition at Walton.

Markham had a thriving social club based in the canteen, which was across the main road from the works. An indoor sports competition was held there each year at Christmas time, consisting of darts, dominoes, cards etc. with cups awarded to the winners. The foremen prided themselves at dominoes and were very upset when Mike Bennett, a mere director, won the cup one year.

Markham sports club held events on the ground across the river from the works. There was the Broad Oaks football team, a bowling green, tennis courts and a rifle club. In 1960, Alan Hare, the personnel manager and an ex-Army man, ran the 0.22 rifle club. Shooting events were held at the Clay Cross Territorial Army drill hall and competition was keen. Ken Wort one evening could not understand how he had managed to get so many shots on target until it was found that Mike Bennett had been peppering the wrong target!

Sports events and social matters were recorded in *Broad Oaks*, a house magazine published twice a year and edited by George Hand's son John.

Social activities dwindled during the 1980s, particularly when the canteen was closed and sold off. It is now the Chesterfield Family Club. The end of the apprenticeship scheme also contributed to the decline.

A point of historical interest relates to the 'Macdonald fund'. J.A. Macdonald was a director of Markham who died on 8 June 1914 and in his will bequeathed part of his estate towards a fund for the benefit of the Markham workforce.

Some of the characters in the last 50 years

Chairmen

Sir Eric Mensforth was the younger son of Sir Holberry Mensforth and was born in Stretford, Manchester, on 17 May 1906. He was educated at Altrincham County High School and University College School and went up to Cambridge as an exhibitioner to King's College where he took a first in Mechanical Sciences. Born in the same year as Robert Barclay, they were contempories at Cambridge. He served his apprenticeship at Mather & Platt and then spent a period working in German factories before returning to join Dorman Long and later English Electric, where he established the domestic appliance division.

70 Sir Eric Mensforth in 1970: precise, energetic and confident.

When John Brown purchased Markham from Staveley in 1937 Mensforth became general manager of Markham. John Brown also purchased another new company, Westland Aircraft of Yeovil, and in 1938 Mensforth was one of a team of young engineers sent at the government's instigation to strengthen Westland Aircraft in the face of likely wartime requirements. Robert Barclay filled the vacancy of general manager at Markham in 1938, he too having worked at English Electric.

Eric Mensforth was appointed managing director at Westland, which built Lysanders and later became an important supplier of Spitfires. In 1943 he was asked to combine his work at Westland with the role of chief production advisor to Sir Stafford Cripps who was Minister of Aircraft Production. His American travels brought him into contact with Sikorsky, which led to Westland's entry into helicopter manufacture. By this time Westland was 50 per cent owned by John Brown and Mensforth moved to Sheffield to take charge of Thomas Firth & John Brown. He became deputy chairman of Markham and subsequently chairman.

Mensforth remained closely associated with Westland, serving as chairman from 1953 to 1968 and as president until 1985. Whilst in Sheffield he was a Deputy Lieutenant of the West Riding and in 1965–6 served as Master Cutler. In 1969 he became the first chairman of governors of Sheffield Polytechnic, now Sheffield Hallam University. He was also chairman of the development council ('Little Neddy') for the engineering industry and of the Council of Engineering Institutions, president of the Institution of Production Engineers, and a founder of the Fellowship of Engineering (later the Royal Academy of Engineering). He was appointed CBE in 1945 and knighted in 1962.

In retirement Sir Eric Mensforth moved from the Sheffield area to live in Epsom, but returned to Sheffield at least once a year and held an informal lunch for friends and old colleagues. Mike Bennett was privileged to be a guest for a number of years up to the last occasion when Sir Eric was 92. He died in 2000 aged 93.

David Nevile Turner was the general manager of the Staveley Company's collieries and was promoted to be managing director of Staveley Coal & Iron and chairman of Markham & Co. on the death of C.P. Markham in 1926. He was appointed chairman of Staveley Coal & Iron in 1935.

Alan Gormly CBE, a chartered accountant, was chairman of Markham from 1983 to 1988. He trained with Peat Marwick (now KMPG) and joined Foster Wheeler John Brown Land Boilers Consortium in 1965. He was subsequently financial director of John Brown Engineering (1970–77) and planning and control director (1977–80). Gormly became deputy chairman of John Brown Engineers & Constructors in 1980 and served as group managing director of John Brown plc from 1983 until 1992. He was chief executive and deputy chairman of the Trafalgar House Group from 1992 until 1994.

Edward Bavister CBE, a chemical engineer, was chairman of Markham from 1988 until 1993, and also deputy managing director of John Brown plc (1987–93) and chairman of Morris Material Handling (1992–99). Ted Bavister was president of the Institution of Chemical Engineers in 1992–3.

Managing Directors

R.J. Barclay, known in the firm as RJB, was born in Glasgow in 1906. He was educated at Repton School and Cambridge, where he obtained an engineering degree. On leaving university in 1927 he joined a small marine engineering concern in Govan where he worked for about five years. He then moved to

71 Robert Barclay, managing director 1941–58, whose office was in the 'Gatehouse'.

English Electric, for whom he also worked for five years and was mainly concerned with high-tension switchgear. It was with English Electric that he first came into contact with hydro-electric power as a result of working on the Galloway scheme, which was the first big Scottish hydro scheme, involving six or seven power stations. On leaving English Electric in 1937 he joined Beardmores and worked there for two years as under-manager of the heavy machine shop. His responsibilities covered the manufacture of large guns, marine work, diesel engine crankshafts and the machining of heavy steel castings.

He joined Markham in March 1939 as general manager under Walter McCartney, in succession to Eric Mensforth. He was general manager for a year and was then appointed a director. When McCartney died in March 1940 RJB was appointed managing director at the age of 34. He served in this capacity until 1958 when he became Markham's deputy chairman until his retirement in 1974. He joined the John Brown Group board in 1958 and was appointed chairman of John Brown SEND. He served in these posts until 1972.

In 1961 RJB was appointed to the board of Foster Wheeler John Brown Land Boilers which shortly afterwards obtained a massive contract for the 500 MW boilers for Tilbury, Eggborough, Ironbridge, Aberthaw, Longanett and Rugeley power stations. This was a very great undertaking and it is a matter of history now that the company had great difficulty in manufacturing the boilers, which were, at that time, among the largest in the world. All were completed satisfactorily. Markham made most of the coal pulverising mills.

RJB was a unique character and his earlier days are best described by his contemporaries and others close to events: see extracts from Sir Eric Mensforth's 'Clogs to Clogs' and stories from the wartime X craft days. He was very active locally and took a great part in the affairs of the neighbourhood. He was a magistrate for 25 years and chairman of the bench for seven.

Ken Wort first met RJB in 1959 when he joined John Brown SEND Ltd as an assistant engineer. RJB was the chairman of SEND and was then comparatively in the management stratosphere! Ken was assigned to Markham as John Brown SEND's liaison engineer for the AGR refuelling machine contract in early 1960. His direct contact was Markham project engineer Mike Bennett who had been recruited from the United Kingdom Atomic Energy Authority (UKAEA) in 1958. So began an association which has lasted 45 years! We had monthly progress meetings with the UKAEA attended by an apparently uninterested RJB. However a week prior to the meeting RJB chaired a pre-progress meeting with Markham and SEND personnel. These meetings were very penetrating and no one was spared if at fault.

Throughout the duration of the very demanding and technically very successful refuelling machine contract RJB was held in the highest esteem by senior UKAEA personnel, albeit tempered with suspicion that he might cut corners in a way that UKAEA beaurocracy could not, justifiably in some instances.

During the installation and commissioning of the refuelling machine at Windscale (now known as Sellafield), RJB insisted on being kept in daily touch with events. This demanded telephone contact twice a day, at lunchtime and in the evenings at dinnertime, simply because RJB knew that he could make contact with Ken at that time of day. RJB's calls lasted from 30 minutes to an hour. He kept a directory of all the pubs in a 15-minute radius from the site so that Ken had no hiding place.

On completion of commissioning Ken was 'donated' to the UKAEA for a year as a walking, talking operations and maintenance manual. This saved the considerable cost of having to write one. RJB had an idiosyncratic approach to office procedure. Eric Langham, consulting electrical engineer to the refuelling machine project, described his interview with RJB in the front office at Broad Oaks. 'I sat at one side of his desk and he at the other. There were three or four mountains of papers on the desk, each at least two feet high, and we had to keep moving position to keep each other in view. I maintained that I had replied to his letter but he didn't think that I had. Eventually he called in his secretary Herbert Hallows. RJB suggested that Hallows look one third of the way down a particular pile, these piles being heaps of files and letters arranged on the floor around the walls of the office. After investigating three piles the letter was found and so apparently the RJB "heap" filing system seemed to work.'

Mike Bennett recalls being involved in another RJB project, the design and installation of a large steel framed plywood clad low speed wind tunnel on the top floor of the Cambridge University engineering laboratory on Trumpington Street. In spite of having a young family Mike had to spend his weekends with RJB and Professor Mair, head of aeronautics at Cambridge. The only recompense was the introduction to some fine wines at the University Arms.

RJB was a meticulous man, almost to the point of eccentricity. He was nevertheless precisely organised, as only a bachelor can be, and a man of system and habit. When in Chesterfield he lived at the Peacock Hotel in Baslow until he was forced to purchase a house, since the Peacock was changing hands. Mike Bennett was involved in a very precise survey and levelling operation of the garden of this new house in Baslow. Mike knows one of his neighbours very well and they began to despair when his garage began to overflow into the drive, caravan and surrounding garden. It was even difficult and dangerous to navigate the stairway to his bedroom.

When in London RJB stayed at Brown's Hotel and he usually travelled up to London by the Master Cutler from Retford on which he was well known to the dining staff. He would be driven from Chesterfield to Retford by his faithful chauffer Albert Parker (not to be confused with Thunderbird's Lady Penelope's Parker).

His belongings, quite apart from two ex-Army Humber estate cars, a saloon car and a motorcycle, which were kept in the Markham garage, filled a good proportion of 'Beckerlegges', a two-storey building opposite the garage, even after he became a John Brown director. He also retained his Chesterfield office base in the 'gatehouse' until Bill Taylor in the 1980s became exasperated and made him vacate the premises. Ken Mullins spent a great deal of his time transferring RJB's belongings to the already overflowing house in Baslow. RJB's vacations were mainly taken in his native Scotland where he owned a yacht and was an ardent deer hunter, with a camera, not a gun.

Although RJB was a stern taskmaster, he was faithful and almost paternal to 'his people'. We found it to be a privilege to work for him.

G.W. Hand. George Hand (GWH) was managing director from 1958 until his retirement in 1968. He had previously been works director at Firth Brown Tools and brought with him Ian Williams who was appointed works director.

GWH had a highly disciplined approach to works housekeeping and to the control of the purse strings, treating Markham money as though it was his own! He had a conservative approach to risk taking—he never took any—and to product development—he hardly did any. He preferred the subcontracting nature of the Boving work and during his time the Kariba dam and the large Spanish turbines were built. Work for Foster Wheeler John Brown Boiler ball and roller mills as well as contracts for DEMAG via John Brown SEND Ltd also ensured that there was no design responsibility. He somewhat grudgingly allowed Mike Bennett, then technical director, to build a test rig and carry out development for the pneumatic conveying business.

For the period of his managing directorship GWH was probably the ideal appointment for Markham. His insistence on the adherence to rigid works housekeeping rules came at the time when Health and Safety requirements were becoming more prominent and his wary attitude to risk, coupled with the fortunate availability of subcontract work, gave Markham a much needed ten years of stability.

GWH was not enthusiastic about the social side of the company and some of the social events withered. He did encourage some of the sporting events and initiated the George Hand Greensomes golf cup. He started the works magazine *Broad Oaks*, edited most ably by his son John who was the commercial manager.

W.H. Taylor. Bill Taylor (WHT) was appointed deputy managing director in mid 1966 and managing director in 1968 when George Hand retired. Bill Taylor had been works manager of the Darlaston steel foundry of F.H. Lloyd, and had been closely involved in the supply of heavy alloy steel castings to Markham for their water turbine contracts. GWH had been impressed by Bill's energy, knowledge and enthusiasm and arranged for him to join Markham.

Bill was a keen and devoted works man, thoroughly understanding all the works processes and quality assurance as well as being well versed in labour relations. He was less at home in the design office and was a little short on patience for sales and commercial work. After Mike Bennett left in 1970, and set up in business as a consulting engineer, Bill offloaded a great deal of the design work to him on an annual retainer basis.

Bill quickly gained an excellent rapport with Boving's management and design teams and Markham's contribution to their design and QA were most valuable on several contracts. For instance, the dumb-bell key, an innovation for clamping together the three 50-ton segments of the El Chocon turbines, was a simple but masterly design—effective and yet economical by reducing the amount of time which the turbine rotors had to spend on expensive machine tools.

Bill's enthusiasm was a key factor in cementing alliances with sister companies, particularly Cravens, and resulted in the acquisition of the Castmaster business and the formation of Bone Markham to manage the paper converting and extrusion coating operation.

The early 1970s was a period of industrial unrest and WHT spent many hours in negotiation with unions, sister companies and local manufacturers to minimise the possibility of disruption to production. It was a measure of his application that Markham suffered only marginally from strike action and that was mostly from token national stoppages.

Bill was the instigator of the development of the works, which involved the continuous introduction of machinery numerical control and in particular the extension of the erecting shop bays, which were equipped with 100-tonne capacity cranes in anticipation of securing larger water turbine work. This was particularly fortuitous for the 1987 order for the Channel tunnel machines, which had sub-assemblies

72 Bill Taylor in Moscow.

weighing almost 100 tonnes.

For the Channel Tunnel job WHT formed an alliance with Dick Robbins and Eric Merrifield of the Robbins Company of Seattle. This relationship blossomed until WHT's retirement in 1988.

WHT was a keen advocate of the social side of the company and fostered inter-departmental sports competitions as well as the Boving-Markham sports day, and Bill and his wife Margery encouraged and supported all Markham social functions.

J.J. Ormston. John Ormston (JO) was recruited to replace Bill Taylor who was to retire and was appointed deputy managing director and later managing director in 1988. JO was a product of the Babcock and Wilcox Group and had risen to become managing director of Jenkins of Retford. He had earlier been involved with the *Mary Rose* preservation project.

JO's style of management was very different to that of WHT with less 'hands on'. Like George Hand he brought his works director David Walker with him from Jenkins and appointed Nick Bristow, who had a coal industry background, as technical director.

An attempt to establish wind energy turbines as a product line was unsuccessful, mainly due to the uncertainty of the home market. The Dunmaglass 600 kW turbine contract ended in a court case won by Markham.

JO's time as managing director coincided with the effective demise of the British coal industry and hence the market for mining machinery. It was also a slack period for water turbines. JO had difficulty in maintaining a viable company and Markham ultimately passed into Davy Metals hands at Sheffield in 1998. The Chesterfield works was closed and a number of the large machines transferred to Sheffield, as were about 130 operatives who were prepared to commute.

Executive directors
Frank Williams (deceased): works; 'Old man Williams', the bowler.
Chris Walters (deceased): commercial.
Ian Williams (deceased): works; 'the trilby'.
Harry Spragg (deceased): stowing.
Reg Dean (deceased): turbines.
Mike Bennett: technical from 1958 to 1970.
John Walmsley (deceased): works.
Ken Wort: commercial from 1967 to 1993.
Ken Randon (deceased): technical.
David Walker: works.
Nick Bristow: technical.
John Hole: personnel.
Malcolm Lindley: financial director and company secretary; accounts.

73 Presentation to Bill McGuire on his retirement. Left to right: Alf Armstrong (chief draughtsman), Mike Bennett (technical director), Bill McGuire, Bill Taylor (managing director).

Non-executive directors
John Baker (Lord Baker), professor of engineering, Cambridge.
Professor David Keith Lucas, RAE Farnborough.
Sir George Gardner, John Brown Engineering.
Professor Sir Joe Pope, Aston University.
Robert Barclay, deputy chairman.
Lord Aberconway (Charles McLaren), chairman of John Brown.

Some of the senior staff

Accounts and commercial: W.H. Platts (company secretary); Ben Raby (company secretary), Stuart Brown (contracts), Gordon Scott (sales), Ted Howson (commercial manager), John Hand (commercial).
   Die-casting: Bernard Martin (manager), Ken Patrick (sales, ex-SEND), Keith Higginbotham (manager, succeeded Bernard Martin), Tony Hobson (sales), John Blankley (installation, commissioning and maintenance engineer).
   Coating and laminating: David Grant (Bone Cravens), Richard Jones (Bone

74 Presentation to Mike Bennett on his leaving Markham. Left to right: Mike Bennett, Alan Ward, Harold Martin, Bill Taylor.

Cravens), Barry Stevens (contracts engineer),

Secretarial and reception: Herbert Hallows (RJB's secretary), Sheila Pemberton (WHT's secretary), Mavis Marmont (WHT's secretary), Miss Sharkey, Phyllis Eldridge, Valerie (receptionists).

Design office: Alf Armstrong (chief draughtsman), John Burton (in charge of the structural drawing office), Jim Bateman (chief draughtsman, mechanical drawing office).

Drawing office: Gordon Booth, Roy Bryan, Chris Bird (Chris took his PhD at Sheffield University on the subject of the strength of tunnel shields and joined Markham after graduating in 1983. He joined Bennett Associates in 1987 becoming a director. He was a member of the design team of the back-up system for the Channel tunnel TBMs then on site for three years.), Dennis Goodhind, David Grainger, Eddie Lawrence, Keith Linney, Bill McGuire, Dudley Nixon, George Norton, George Pell, Jim Robotham, Mike Robotham, John Salt, Peter Spiegel, Alec Wyatt, and Arthur Richardson (print room and photography, ex-Grenadier Guards and former professional footballer).

Estimating department: Charlie Brumby, John Cook, Walter Dunn, Geoff Evans, Eric Marsden, Eric Naylor, George Whysall, Reg Wright.

Turbine department: John Barson, Harry Parsons.

Stowing department: Ernest Goodwin, Harold Heath, Dennis Longmate, Ken Mullins, Noel Wilde.

Tunnelling department: Richard Lewis, John Foster, Brian Honeyben, all ex-Priestley. Bob Wood was technical manager for the RMJV Channel Tunnel project and is now employed by Bennett Associates.

Buying department: Ken Lane, Terry Jackson.

Accounts department: Alan Ward, John Whysall, Harold Martin

Works management and administration

Some of the works staff included Fred Cresswell (works progress), Roy Cherry (works methods), Frank Cherry (quality assurance), Alan Hare and Eric Alsop (personnel), Jack Brown, David Wilkinson and Hugh McCaig (outside erection), Betty, Mary and Mrs Goodison (Goody) (catering, managers' mess and directors' dining room).

Some of the workforce

Arthur Rayner (hauling shop foreman), Jack Clarke, Sam Brocksopp (senior foreman), Frank Slawson (fitting shop foreman), Tom Brocklehurst (foreman), Frank Tagg (foreman for apprentices), Jack Booker, the Madison family (Teddy (senior foreman fitting shop), Mick and Neil), Monty Harrold, Jack Reynolds, Dennis Crich, Chris Peacock, Walt Edson, George Ison, Colin Burton, George Evans and Algy Hall (fitting shop), Ross Madison (small machine shop foreman), Stan Ball (boiler shop and sales), George Slack (fabrication shop foreman), Sam Wheatcroft (fabrication shop foreman, followed George Slack), Vic Coles (fabrication shop welder), Clive Shaw (foreman pattern maker), Ivan Tagg (maintenance), Albert Parker, Terry Moore (works chauffeurs), Arthur Large, Denis Gosmark (transport).

Appendices

Appendix 1: Water turbines manufactured since October 1928

Name of Plant	Type of turbine	Pressure head units	Total output (kW)	No. of units	kW per unit	Country
Waipori No. 1, 1929	Francis	29	4,774	1	4,774	New Zealand
Waipori No. 1, 1929	Francis	29	4,774	1	4,774	New Zealand
Mansam, 1930	Francis	73	4,476	1	4,476	Burma
Lochaber Aux, 1932	Pelton	220	2,760	2	1,380	Scotland
Cuando River, 1929	Francis	30	560	2	280	Africa
Grampian Temp, 1929	Francis	30	560	2	280	Scotland
Waipori 4th	Pelton	203	4,103	1	4,103	New Zealand
Palestine 1 and 2, 1929	Francis	27	12,682	2	6,341	Palestine
Reading,1929	Francis	1	90	3	30	England
Glen Morgan	Pelton	190	746	2	373	Scotland
Onakaka	Pelton	183	298	1	298	New Zealand
Waitaki Main	Francis	21	34,316	2	17,158	New Zealand
Waipori 5th	Pelton	203	4,103	1	4,103	New Zealand
Mt Lyall	Pelton	320	1,306	1	1,306	Tasmania
Glen Morgan Extn	Pelton	190	373	1	373	Scotland
Arnold River, 1930	Kaplan	11–14	3,282	2	1,641	New Zealand
Waitaki Aux	Francis	18	896	2	448	New Zealand
Shanan Main, 1930	Pelton	509	50,728	4	12682	India
Shanan Aux, 1931	Pelton	508	541	1	541	India
Arapuni	Francis	52	970	2	485	New Zealand
Tummel, 1932	Francis	117	35,808	2	17,904	Scotland
Konnyaung	Francis	48	2,723	1	2,723	Burma
Palestine 3rd	Francis	27	6,341	1	6,341	Palestine
Sivasamudram 8th	Francis	127	6,714	1	6,714	India
Maentwrog, 1929	Pelton	183	6,714	1	6,714	Wales
Cwn Dyli, 1934	Pelton	305	3,857	1	3,857	Wales
Arapuni 7 and 8, 1935	Francis	51	44,768	2	22,384	New Zealand
Tarraleah	Pelton	287	46,998	3	15,666	Tasmania
Burrinjuck	Francis	59	10,742	2	5371	Australia
Dolgarrog	Pelton	323	8,504	1	8,504	Wales
Sivasamudram 9th	Francis	127	6,714	1	6,714	India
Milton Mill	Francis	4	3	1	3	England
Waikaremoana	Francis	192	20,888	1	20,888	New Zealand
Jekko, 1937	Pelton	184	4625	1	4625	Nigeria
Hpaungdaw	Pelton	427	3,132	3	1,044	Burma
Shimsha	Francis	182	18,202	2	9,101	India
Arapuni 5 and 6	Francis	51	44,768	2	22,384	New Zealand
Waipori 6 and 7	Pelton	202	8,206	2	4,103	New Zealand

Name of Plant	Type of turbine	Pressure head units	Total output (kW)	No. of units	kW per unit	Country
Kaitawa	Francis	31	33,570	2	16,785	Sumatra
Cuando Extn, 1940	Francis	30	280	1	280	Africa
Karapiro	Kaplan	30–31	31,332	3	10,444	New Zealand
Jog falls	Pelton	356	56,800	4	14,200	India
Pallivasal	Pelton	609	15,816	2	7,908	India
Pallivasal	Pelton	609	7,908	1	7,908	India
Jog falls Extension	Pelton	356	96,980	4	24,245	India
Pyakoshi (runner)	Kaplan	33	38,195	1	38,195	Finland
Waitaki	Francis	21	17,158	1	17,158	New Zealand
Mankala (runner)	Kaplan	10	30,996	3	10,332	Finland
Kiewa (and runner)	Francis	187	47,559	3	15,853	Australia
Moyar	V Pelton	376	40,284	3	13,428	India
Eildon	Francis	72	120	2	60	Australia
Abjora	Pelton	384	82,506	3	27,502	Norway
Moshi	Pelton	?	1,342	2	671	Nigeria
Muyuka	Francis	11	1,596	2	798	Nigeria
Los Peares	Francis	85	165,165	3	55,055	Spain
Salto De Castro	Francis	34	88,028	2	44,014	Spain
Owen Falls	Kaplan	6	62,664	4	15,666	Uganda
Tungatinah	Francis	?	130,550	5	26,110	New Zealand
Waitaki 6 and 7	Francis	21	34,316	2	17,158	New Zealand
Waipori 3 and 4	Francis	54	14,130	2	7,065	New Zealand
Kiewa No. 1	V Pelton	473	67,140	4	16,785	Australia
Owen Falls 5 and 6	Kaplan	6	31,332	2	15,666	Uganda
Eildan	Francis	72	122,642	2	61,321	Australia
Port Moresby	Francis	?	3,246	3	1,082	New Guinea
Dolgarrog	Francis	262	10,444	1	10,444	Wales
Kiewa Nos. 1, 5 and 6	V Pelton	473	33,570	2	16,785	Australia
Eurene	Francis	244	55,950	2	27,975	Spain
Waipapa	Kaplan	16	53,712	3	17,904	New Zealand
Kariba	Francis	110	522,200	5	104,440	Rhodesia
Belessar	Francis	101	203,658	3	67,886	Spain
Dinas	Francis	?	12,682	1	12,682	Spain
Aratiatia	Francis	34	93,996	3	31,332	New Zealand
Murray 1	Francis	491	775,840	8	96,980	Australia
Velle	Kaplan	14	83,552	2	41,776	Spain
Castrello	Kaplan	21	116,376	2	58,188	Spain
Frieira	Kaplan	26	143,232	2	71,616	Spain
Meadowbanks	Kaplan	28	41,776	1	41,776	Spain
Repulse	Kaplan	25	29,094	1	29,094	Spain
Cluky	Kaplan	14	17,531	1	17,531	Spain
Kariba	Francis	104	104,440	1	104,440	Rhodesia
Poatina	Pelton	808	307,725	5	61,545	Tasmania
Murray 1	Francis	491	194,000	2	97,000	Australia
Owen Falls 9 and 10	Kaplan	19	31,232	2	15,616	Uganda
Kindaruma	Kaplan	32	41,776	2	20,888	Kenya
Waipori	Francis	195	18,575	1	18,575	New Zealand

Name of Plant	Type of turbine	Pressure head units	Total output (kW)	No. of units	kW per unit	Country
Devils Gate	Francis	67	62,664	1	62,664	Tasmania
Villarino	Fran. pump	402	288,702	2	144,351	Spain
Paloona	Kaplan	31	30,026	1	30,026	Tasmania
El Chocon 1 to 4	Francis	59	816,000	4	204,000	Argentine
Foyers	Fran. pump	165	304,400	2	152,200	Scotland
Porabka-Zar 4	Fran. pump	457	540,000	4	135,000	Poland
El Chocon 5 and 6	Fran. pump	59	414,800	2	207,400	Argentine
Kangaroo Valley	Francis	488	194,000	2	97,000	Australia
Camlough	Fran. pump	155	232,800	2	116,400	Ireland
Planicie Banderita	Francis	68	466,000	2	233,000	Argentine
Kadamparai	Pump	341	200,000	2	100,000	India
Dartmouth	Francis	159	153,080	1	153,080	Australia
Dinorwic	Pump	537	1,902,300	6	317,050	Wales
Kpong	Propeller	12	81,600	2	40,800	Ghana
Roseires	Kaplan	33	88,000	2	44,000	Sudan
Nagarjungasagar North bank	Kaplan	25	61,200	2	30,600	India
Lupohlo-Ezulwini	Pelton	232	20,800	2	10,400	Swaziland
Victoria	Francis	190	166,000	2	83,000	Sri Lanka
R.W. Mathews	Hor. Fran.	29	2,000	2	1,000	USA
OK Menga	Francis	192	59,680	2	29840	Papua
Kielder	Kaplan	45	5,000	1	5,000	UK
Indian Valley	Hor. Fran.	47	3,000	2	1,500	USA
Collywobbles	Francis	135	43,500	3	14,500	Transkei
Mount Ida	Hor. Fran.	47	3,000	2	1,500	USA
Saujatu	Hor. Fran.	120	3,600	2	1,800	W. Samoa
Mrica	Francis	85	184,500	3	61,500	Indonesia
Proctor	Francis	35	3,000	1	3,000	USA
Miramar	Hor. Fran.	22	800	2	400	USA
Alvrado	Hor. Fran.	61	2,400	2	1,200	USA
Siskiyou	Hor. Fran.	53	6,800	2	3,400	USA
Caemsa	Hor. Fran.	27	2,200	1	2,200	Chile
Farmers 1 MW	Hor. Fran.	111	1,000	1	1000	USA
Farmers 2 MW	Hor. Fran.	111	2,000	1	2000	USA
Galesville	Hor. Fran.	37	1,800	2	900	USA
San Gabriel 1	Hor. Fran.	84	4,700	1	4,700	USA
San Gabriel 2	Hor. Fran.	73	2,400	2	1200	USA
Middle Fork	Hor. Fran.	50	500	1	500	USA
Jean	Pelton	295	3,200	2	1,600	Peru
Sandia	Pelton	213	2,400	2	1,200	Peru
Caclic	Hor. Fran.	70	5,200	4	1,300	Peru
Wise 2	Hor. Fran.	141	2,900	1	2,900	USA
Nanpil River 1	Hor. Fran.	61	650	1	650	Micronesia
Nanpil River 2	Hor. Fran.	61	1,150	1	1,150	Micronesia
Sengguruh	Kaplan	18.5	30,200	2	15,100	Indonesia
Roseires No. 7	Kaplan	33	44,000	1	44,000	Sudan
Videlia	Bulb	5.33	100,000	4	25,000	USA

Name of Plant	Type of turbine	Pressure head units	Total output (kW)	No. of units	kW per unit	Country
Yonki Dam	Francis	185	30,000	2	15000	Indonesia
Nagarjungasagar						
Left bank	Kaplan	20	49,400	2	24,700	India
Right bank	Kaplan	25	30,600	1	30,600	India
Pergau	–	–	–	–	–	–

The total installed capacity was 10,445 MW of which 3,000 MW was for the UK. In all 275 turbines were made.

Appendix 2: Tunnelling equipment manufactured since 1887

No. of units	Description of plant	Diameter/ size	Customer	Project
20	Rock drills	–	A. Schram & Co.	
8	Shields	?	J.W. Williams	
1	Shield	?	W. Scott & Co.	
2	Shields	5.3	Kennedy & Sons	
6	Shields	3.72	C. Brand & Sons	
1	Shield	3.72	J. Patterson & Sons	
4	Shields	3.72	C. Brand & Sons	
1	Shield	2.56	J.B. Berlier	
1	Shield	3.72	D. Shanks	
1	Shield	5.7	North British Railway Co.	
1	Shield	3.4	J. Birch & Co.	
1	Shield	1.9	Aird & Son	
4	Shields	4	John Mowlem & Co. Ltd	
11	Shields	3.86	W. Scott & Co.	
3	Shields	3.86	John Price	
2	Shields	4.02	George Talbot	
3	Shields	6.8	W. Scott & Co.	Central London
3	Shields	6.8	John Price	Central London
1	Shield	3.86	John Price	Notting Hill Station
6	Shields	3.86	John Mowlem & Co. Ltd	
1	Shield	3.11	F. Taylor	
6	Shields	3.86	W. Scott & Co.	
2	Shields	6.8	John Mowlem & Co. Ltd	
1	Shield	6.8	John Price	
1	Shield	8.18	George Talbot	
1	Shield	4.09	George Talbot	
2	Shields	7.58	Perry & Co.	
13	Shields	3.95	Perry & Co.	

No. of units	Description of plant	Diameter/ size	Customer	Project
1	Shield	6.8	George Talbot	
4	Shields	6.8	W. Rigby	
1	Shield	9.86	W. Rigby	
3	Shields	6.8	Perry & Co.	Baker St, Waterloo line
2	Shields	3.48	W. Rigby	
1	Shield	3.96	J. Cochrane	
1	Shield	3.17	W. Middlesex Waterworks	
4	Shields	5.3	S. Pearson	
7	Shields	6.8	Walker Price & Reeves	
19	Excavator shields	3.86	Price & Reeves	
1	Shield	4.16	Walker Price & Reeves	
3	Shields	6.8	W. Scott & Middleton	
1	Patent excavator	?	J. Price	
1	Shield	4.14	Price & Reeves	Charing Cross
2	Shields	3.86	Price & Reeves	Piccadilly Circus
1	Shield	3.86	Edmund Nuttall	
3	Shields	4.16	Walker Price & Reeves	
7	Shields	3.95	John Mowlem & Co. Ltd	
1	Special shield	?	John Mowlem & Co. Ltd	
14	Excavator shields	3.86	J. Price	
1	Shield	2.69	R. McAlpine	
2	Excavator shields	3.86	W. Scott Middleton	
1	Excavator shield	4.16	Walker Price & Reeves	
1	Shield	4.93	London County Council	
1	Shield	2.69	Peter Lanse	
1	Shield	6.8	Price & Reeves	
1	Shield	9.34	Price & Reeves	
1	Shield	2.73	John Mowlem & Co. Ltd	Rotherhithe
3	Excavator shields	3.5	W. Scott Middleton	
1	Shield	2.19	C.C. Lindsay, Price & Reeves	
2	Shields	5.31	Jean Berliner, France	Paris Metro
1	Excavator shield	3.5	W. Scott & Middleton	
3	Shields	2.85	Tilbury Dredging	
1	Shield	9.35	Price & Reeves	Rotherhithe
1	Shield	2.11	John Mowlem & Co. Ltd	
1	Shield	2.34	Price & Reeves	
6	Shields	3.05	Griffiths & Co.	
9	Shields	3.96	John Mowlem & Co. Ltd	
3	Shields	6.8	John Mowlem & Co. Ltd	Charing Cross and Paddington

No. of units	Description of plant	Diameter/ size	Customer	Project
6	Shields	3.94	W. Scott & Middleton	
1	Shield	6.8	W. Scott & Middleton	
1	Shield	2.06	J.C. White	
2	Shields	2.7	J. Cochrane	
9	Shields	3.03	W. Scott & Middleton	Post Office
8	Excavator shields	1.52	War Office	
1	Shield	2.72	J. Cochrane	
1	Shield	3.9	C.S.L. Ryley	
1	Excavator shield	3.86	W. Scott & Middleton	
11	Shields	3.9	City & London Railways	
6	Shields	3.86	John Mowlem & Co. Ltd	Camden Town extn.
6	Shields	3.86	C. Brand & Sons	City & South extn.
10	Shields	3.9	City & South Railways	
4	Shields	3.9	Perry & Co.	
2	Shields	3.86	Foundation Ltd.	
3	Shields	4.12	John Mowlem & Co. Ltd	
1	Excavator shield	3.86	United Construction	
1	Shield	3.35	J. Cochrane	
1	Shield	3.86	United Construction	
10	Excavator shields	3.86	London Electric Railway	
6	Excavator shields	6.8	London Electric Railway	
8	Shields	4.12	Metropolitan Tunnel	Charing Cross, Kensington extn.
2	Shields	6.8	Metropolitan Tunnel	
2	Shields	3.29	W. Scott & Middleton	
2	Shields	2.21	W. Scott & Middleton	
4	Shields	3.86	C. Brand & Sons	
1	Shield	6.8	C. Brand & Sons	
1	Shield	5.79	Metropolitan Tunnel	
1	Shield	2.39	John Mowlem & Co. Ltd	
1	Shield	2.82	Calabro-LucanaRailway	Italy
2	Shields	3.66	Foundation Ltd	
1	Shield	1.8	Foundation Ltd	
10	Erector shields	?	Edmund Nuttall	Mersey Tunnel
3	Shields	2.95	Foundation Ltd	Mersey Tunnel
1	Shield	2.13	J. Cochrane	
3	Erector shields	?	R. McAlpine	
1	Shield	13.41	Edmund Nuttall	Mersey Tunnel
2	Shields	3.35	John Mowlem & Co. Ltd	
1	Shield	4.86	S.A. Funicular	Barcelona Metro
18	Shields	3.96	London Electric Railway	Finsbury Park

No. of units	Description of plant	Diameter/ size	Customer	Project
2	Shields	9.11	C. Brand & Sons	
2	Shields	3.16	C. Brand & Sons	
6	Shields	7.57	C. Brand & Sons	
1	Shield	2.39	Enterprises Desplates	France
1	Shield	6.97	C. Brand & Sons	
2	Shields	2.54	John Mowlem & Co. Ltd	
2	Shields	2.13	Kinnear Moodie	
1	Shield	6.6	Arcos Ltd	Moscow Metro
1	Shield	1.98	Howard Farrow	
1	Shield	4.81	London Electric Railway	
1	Shield	1.66	Howard Farrow	
2	Shields	2.21	Kinnear Moodie	
2	Shields	3.35	R. McAlpine	
1	Shield	1.98	Howard Farrow	
2	Shields	3.05	C. Brand & Sons	
1	Shield	?	Crown Agents for Colonies	Trinidad Waterworks
1	Shield	1.9	Metropolitan Construction	
10	Shields	3.96	John Mowlem & Co. Ltd	
1	Shield	2.13	John Mowlem & Co. Ltd	
1	Excavator shield	3.86	C. Brand & Sons	
4	Shields	9.8	Mott-Hay & Anderson	Dartford to Purfleet
12	Shields	3.96	London Passenger Transport	
2	Shields	6.97	London Passenger Transport	London Underground
1	Shield	3.86	South Essex Water Co.	
1	Shield	3.71	John Mowlem & Co. Ltd	
1	Shield	3.33	Holloway Brothers	
1	Shield	4.09	Holloway Brothers	
1	Shield	3.96	Balfour Beatty & Co. Ltd	
1	Shield	3.5	A. Waddington	
1	Shield	3	Peterson Dickinson	
1	Shield	1.98	Durban Corporation	South Africa
1	Shield	2.21	Patterson Denton	
1	Shield	2.15	A. Waddington	
1	Shield	3.2	Yorkshire Hennebique	
3	Slurry TBMs	6	Mitchell Construction	Mexico City sewers
1	Shield	2.67	Anglo-Scottish Plant	Portsmouth sewage
1	Shield	3.43	Anglo-Scottish Plant	Gothenburg, Sweden
1	Drum Digger	3.98	Kinnear Moodie	Barcelona, Spain
1	Shield	1.58	Anglo-Scvottish Plant	
3	Shields	4.14	C.Brand & Sons	London Underground
2	Shields	10.48	Balfour Beatty & Co. Ltd	2nd Dartford tunnel
1	Shield	2.8	John Mowlem & Co. Ltd	Falconbrook sewer
1	Walking roadway support	5.23 × 3.66	National Coal Board	
2	Excavator shields	2.84	John Mowlem & Co. Ltd	Carsington aqueduct

No. of units	Description of plant	Diameter/ size	Customer	Project
2	Excavator shields	2.6	John Mowlem & Co. Ltd	Newcastle sewer
1	Excavator shield	2.82	Thyssen GB	
1	Excavator shield	2.82	Miller Buckley Civil Eng. Ltd	
1	Hard rock TBM	2.16	Fairclough Civil Eng. Ltd	
1	Hard rock TBM	4.19	Lodigiani SPA	Milan, Italy
1	SARS[1]	3.95 × 5.63	National Coal Board	
1	SARS	3.95 × 5.63	National Coal Board	
1	AFERS[2]	3.67 × 4.96	National Coal Board	
1	SAFERS[3]	4.0 × 5.63	National Coal Board	
2	SAFERS	3.67 × 4.96	National Coal Board	
1	ARS[4]	3.95 × 5.63	National Coal Board	
1	SAFERS	3.95 × 5.63	National Coal Board	
2	Slurry TBMs	5.15	Lilley Construction	Cairo, Egypt
1	Slurry TBM	6.11	Lilley Construction	Cairo
1	SAFERS	3.95 × 5.63	National Coal Board	
1	Segment erector		Robbins Co.	
2	TBMs	8.36	TML	Channel Tunnel
2	SAFERS	3.95 × 5.63	British Coal	North Western area
1	EPB pipe jack TBM	1.46	Tube Headings	
1	Super mini 500 TBM	0.66	Miller Markham	
2	Jacking shields	6.34	British Coal	
1	Shield back-up system		AMCO	
1	EPB pipe jack TBM	1.46	Sade	
1	Super mini 500 TBM	0.66	Miller Markham	For hire
1	EPB TBM	5.35	GTM	
2	Hard rock TBM	5.03	Robbins Co.	Lesotho Highlands
1	Super mini 500 TBM	0.66	Sade	

[1] Self-advancing roadway support.
[2] Advanceable face-end roadway support.
[3] Self-advancing face-end roadway support.
[4] Advanceable roadway support.

No. of units	Description of plant	Diameter/ size	Customer	Project
1	Roadheader with poling plates	6.55	Metrosud	Naples
1	Roadheader with poling plates	6.55	Metrosud	Naples
1	Super mighty 1000 micro-tunnelling TBM	1.2	Miller Markham	
1	Hard rock TBM	5.03	Robbins Co.	Bukak
1	Hard rock TBM	3.2	Robbins Co.	Hinteregger
1	Hard rock TBM refurb	3.26	Balfour Beatty	Jersey
1	Cutterhead for hard rock TBM	5.03	Robbins Co.	Lötschberg
1	Super mighty 1000 micro-tunnelling TBM	1.2	Laxfield Corporation	
1	Super mini 500 TBM	0.66	Laxfield Corporation	
1	Hard rock TBM	7.00	Robbins Co.	New York
1	Lining replacement shield	5.08	AME Civil Engineering	London
1	Hard rock TBM	4.02	Robbins Co.	Renun
1	Expansion kit for hard rock TBM	4.02	Robbins Co.	Renun
2	Hard rock TBMs	4.90	Atlas Copco Robbins	Boston, USA
1	Slurry TBM	5.85	Kawasaki H I	DLR, London
1	Hard rock TBM	10.00	Atlas Copco Robbins	Manapouri

516 shields and TBMs were made, of which some 287 were for the London Underground.

Appendix 3: Mine hoists manufactured since 1869

Date	Type of drum	Drum Dia. m	Drum width m	Drum cap. sq.m	Cyl. dia in.	Cyl. stroke in.	kW	Customer
1869	Single drum	3.00			26	60		Pilsley
1870					20	48		Clay Cross
1871	Single drum	3.40	2.1	22.4	26	54		Clay Cross
1872	Single drum	8.50			36	72		Holmewood
1873					26	54		Pilsley
1874	Single drum	6.60			36	72		Grassmoor
1877	Single drum	5.90	2.1	38.9	36	72		Silverhill
1880					40	72		Hudson & Co.
1880	Single drum	5.90	2.6	48.2	40	72		Langwith
1881	Single drum	4.30			30	60		Vancouver Coal Co., Canada
1885	Single drum	5.50	3.2	55.3	30	60		Grassmoor
1886					30	72		Alfreton
1889	Single drum	3.00	2.7	25.4	22	48		T. Olivery & Sons
1889	Single drum	7.30			36	72		Whitwell
1890	Double drum	4.30	1.5	20.3	30	60		Langwith
1890					34	60		E.M. Mundy
1890					34	60		Shipley
1892	Single drum	5.50	3.0	51.8	40	72		Babbington, Tibshelf colliery
1892	Single drum	2.10			12	24		Grassmoor
1892	Single drum	2.70			18	36		Grassmoor
1892	Single drum	2.10			22	48		Hickleton
1893	Conical drum	4.90	5.2	80.0	32	72		Nunnery
1893	Conical drum	6.40	7.0	140.7	42	84		Warsop Main
1895	Single drum	6.70	2.3	48.4	48	72		Harton Coal Co., Whitburn
1895	Conical drum	5.50	9.1	157.2	42	72		South Kirkby
1895	Conical drum	4.40	4.9	67.7	36	72		Sutton
1896	Single drum	5.80	2.6	47.4	36	72		Markham
1896	Single drum	3.00	1.1	10.4	20	60		F.A. Robinson & Co.
1896	Conical drum	5.50	6.1	105.4	36	72		Shirebrook
1897	Single drum	6.10	4.0	76.7	48	90		Grimethorpe
1897	Single drum	3.40	2.3	24.6	24	60		Maclaren
1899	Single drum	4.60	2.5	36.1	28	72		Dalmellington Iron Co.
1899	Single drum	7.40	3.6	83.7	48	90		Shirebrook
1899	Single drum	6.10	2.4	46.0	36	72		Wombwell
1900					25	48		Calow Main
1900	Single drum	3.70	2.0	23.2	20	48		Crigglestone Coal Co.
1900	Single drum	4.90	2.4	36.9	32	72		Manvers Main
1900	Single drum	6.40	3.0	60.3	36	72		Warsop Main
1900	Single drum	6.10	3.8	72.8	42	84		Windsor Steam Coal
1902	Single drum	4.30	2.4	32.4	32	72		Dean & Chapter
1902	Single drum	5.50	?		36	72		Grimethorpe
1902	Single drum	6.10	3.7	70.9	42	84		Williamthorpe
1903							112	British Westinghouse
1903					24	42		Clay Cross
1903	Single drum	6.10			42	84		Silverwood
1903	Conical drum	5.20	6.1	99.7	36	78		Victoria
1904	Single drum	6.70	3.7	77.9	40	84		Dinnington Main
1904	Single drum	7.30	3.7	84.9	48	90		Frickley
1905	Single drum	6.10	3.3	63.2	32	72		Hanley Deep
1905	Conical drum	5.30	5.9	98.2	32	72		Mansfield
1905	Conical drum	5.80	7.9	143.9	42	84		Manton
1905	Conical drum	7.30	3.4	78.0	42	84		Sneyd
1906	Conical drum	5.30	9.1	151.5	46	90		Brodsworth
1906	Single drum	6.12	3.4	65.4	38	78		Clock Face

Date	Type of drum	Drum Dia. m	Drum width m	Drum cap. sq.m	Cyl. dia in.	Cyl. stroke in.	kW	Customer
1906	Single drum	1.80			?	?	187	Tredegar
1907	Single drum	4.90	2.7	41.6	32.0	72		Crumlin
1907	Conical drum	4.30	6.7	90.5	36	72		Crumlin
1907	Conical drum	5.20	8.4	137.2	42.0	84		Oakdale Navigation
1907	Single drum	7.30	?		42.0	84		Yorkshire Main
1907	Conical drum	5.50	10.4	179.7	42.0	84		Yorkshire Main
1908	Single drum	3.70	2.4	27.9	22	48		Bowes & Partners
1908	Single drum	5.80	2.1	38.3	30	72		Bullcroft Main
1908	Single drum	6.10	?		37	78		Clock Face
1909	Single drum	3.00	2.0	18.8	22	48		Hartley Bank
1909	Single drum	4.90	2.6	40.0	30	72		Horden
1909	Single drum	5.50	3.5	60.5	36	72		Horden
1909	Single drum	5.50	3.5	60.5	36	72		Horden
1909	Conical drum	5.50	9.1	157.2	40	84		South Kirkby
1909	Conical drum	4.90	8.5	130.8	38	78		Thurcroft
1910	Single drum	6.10	3.0	57.5	32	72		East Kent
1910	Conical drum	1.80	4.6	26.0			224	Maclaren
1910	Conical drum	5.20	9.8	160.1	44	84		Maltby
1910	Single drum	4.30	2.9	39.2	30	60		Manvers Main
1910	Single drum	4.30	2.9	39.2	30	60		Manvers Main
1910	Single drum	4.30	2.9	39.2	30	60		Manvers Main
1910	Conical drum	3.70	5.0	58.1				Markham Steam Coal
1910	Conical drum	3.70	5.0	58.1				Markham Steam Coal
1910	Conical drum	3.00	4.6	43.4	22	60		Oakdale Navigation
1910	Single drum	4.30	?		30	60		Snowden
1910	Single drum	5.50	2.3	39.7	36	66		Wheatsheaf
1911	Conical drum	4.30	6.7	90.5	36	72		Barnburgh
1911					36	72		Cefncoed
1911	Conical drum	4.30	7.3	98.6	38	72		Coventry
1911	Single drum	6.10	2.7	51.7	40	78		Hickleton
1911	Single drum	6.10	2.7	51.7	36	72		Hickleton
1911	Single drum	3.70			24	48		Holroyd
1911	Single drum	4.90	2.9	44.6	26	60		Oakdale Navigation
1911	Single drum	6.10	2.6	49.8	32	72		Rufford
1911	Single drum	6.10	2.6	49.8	36	84		Rufford
1911	Single drum	3.40					783	Gwaun-Cae-Gurwen
1912	Single drum	4.00	2.0	25.1	28	60		Allerton Bywater
1912	Conical drum	4.30	7.3	98.6	34	72		Dinnington Main
1912	Conical drum	4.30	6.7	90.5	38	78		Frickley
1913	Conical drum	3.00	6.1	57.5			522	Blackhall
1913	Conical drum	3.00	6.1	57.5			522	Blackhall
1913	Conical drum	4.30	7.3	98.6	36	84		Brodsworth
1913	Single drum	6.10	3.5	67.1	26	84		Kirkby
1913	Conical drum	2.70	4.9	41.6			410	Lingdale
1913	Conical drum	4.90	8.5	130.8	36	84		Llay Main
1913	Conical drum	4.90	8.5	130.8	36	84		Llay Main
1914	Single drum	6.10	2.6	49.8	36	84		Clipstone
1914	Single drum	2.40	2.0	15.1	20	36		Holroyd
1914	Single drum	2.40	2.0	15.1	36	36		Holroyd
1914	Conical drum	4.30	7.3	98.6	36	72		Manton
1914	Conical drum	5.20	9.8	160.1	44	84		Rossington
1914	Conical drum	4.30	7.3	98.6	36	72		Stonehall
1914	Single drum	5.50	2.7	46.7	30	72		Swanwick
1915	Conical drum	4.30	6.7	90.5	32	72		Coppice
1915	Single drum	3.00	2.0	18.8	16	48		Ramcroft
1916	Single drum	6.40	2.6	52.3	34	78		Markham Main
1916	Single drum	6.40	2.6	52.3	34	78		Markham Main
1916	Single drum	3.70	2.3	26.7	26	54		Shotton

Date	Type of drum	Drum Dia. m	Drum width m	Drum cap. sq.m	Cyl. dia in.	Cyl. stroke in.	kW	Customer
1919	Single drum	2.70	0.9	7.6	16	48		Brodsworth
1919	Single drum	2.70	2.1	17.8			328	Dowell
1919	Single drum	2.70	2.1	17.8			328	Dowell
1919	Single drum	3.00	2.0	18.8			373	Hickleton
1919	Single drum	3.00	2.0	18.8			373	Hickleton
1919	Single drum	6.10	3.5	67.1	36	84		Ollerton
1919	Single drum	6.10	3.5	67.1	36	84		Ollerton
1919	Conical drum	4.90	8.5	130.8	40	84		Parsonage
1919	Single drum	2.90	2.0	18.2	20	36		Ty-Trist
1920	Single drum	4.30	2.7	36.5	26	60		Aitken
1920	Single drum	3.00	2.0	18.8			373	Consett Iron Co.
1920	Conical drum	4.90	8.5	130.8	36	84		Hickleton
1920	Conical drum	4.90	8.5	130.8	36	84		Oakdale Navigation
1920	Single drum	4.90	2.1	32.3	30	72		Pochin
1921	Conical drum	3.40	4.9	52.3			821/1388	Mountain Ash
1921	Single drum	6.40	3.0	60.3	36	84		Pleasley
1922	Conical drum	4.30	7.3	98.6	36	84		Brodsworth
1922	Single drum	4.20	2.0	26.4	24	54		Harrycroft
1922	Single drum	6.10	2.4	46.0	38	78		New Monkton
1923	Conical drum	4.90	8.5	130.8	36	84		Betteshanger
1923	Conical drum	4.90	8.5	130.8	36	84		Betteshanger
1923	Conical drum	4.90	8.5	130.8	36	84		Blidworth
1923	Conical drum	4.90	8.5	130.8	36	84		Blidworth
1923	Conical drum	4.90	8.5	130.8	36	84		Firbeck
1923	Conical drum	4.90	8.5	130.8	36	84		Firbeck
1923	Single drum	5.80	2.6	47.4	30	72		Glapwell
1923	Single drum	5.80	2.6	47.4	30	72		Markham
1924	Single drum	6.10	3.4	65.2	36	84		Bolsover
1924	Conical drum	4.90	8.5	130.8	36	84		Houghton Main
1924	Conical drum	4.90	8.5	130.8	36	84		Newstead
1924	Conical drum	4.90	8.5	130.8	36	84		Upton
1924	Conical drum	4.90	8.5	130.8	36	84		Upton
1925	Conical drum	4.30	6.7	90.5	36	72		Barnburgh
1925	Single drum	6.10	3.0	57.5	36	84		Bilsthorpe
1925	Conical drum	4.90	7.9	121.6			2238/3879	Grimethorpe
1925	Conical drum	3.70	5.5	63.9			1194	Wyllie
1925	Conical drum	3.70	5.5	63.9			1194	Wyllie
1926	Single drum	2.70	1.7	14.4			112	Markham Main
1927	Double drum	4.30	1.7	23.0	40	72		Randfontein Gold Mines, SA
1927	Double drum	3.70	1.2	13.9				East Rand Mines, SA
1927	Double drum	3.70	1.2	13.9				East Rand Mines, SA
1927	Double drum	3.70	1.2	13.9				East Rand Mines, SA
1927	Double drum	3.70	1.2	13.9				Consolidated Main Reef, SA
1927	Double drum	4.30	1.7	23.0	38	72		New States Areas, SA
1929	Double drum	4.30	1.7	23.0	38	72		Randfontein Gold Mines
1930	Double drum	3.40	1.4	15.0			127	Arcos
1930	Single drum	6.10	2.6	49.8	36	84		New Monkton
1930	Double drum	4.90	1.7	26.2				Crown Mines, SA
1931	Double drum	5.20	1.6	26.1			298	Arcos
1931	Double drum	3.40	2.5	26.7	25			Daggerfontein Mines, SA
1931	Double drum	3.40	2.5	26.7	40			Daggerfontein Mines, SA
1931	Double drum	3.40	2.5	26.7	60			Daggerfontein Mines, SA
1931	Conical drum	4.00	5.5	69.1	32	72		Denaby and Cadeby
1932	Conical drum	2.60	3.4	27.8			276/621	Ellington
1933	Double drum	3.70	1.2	13.9			858	Consolidated Main Reef, SA
1933	Double drum	4.90	1.7	26.2			1380	Crown Mines, SA
1933	Double drum	4.90	1.7	26.2				Crown Mines, SA
1933	Single drum	2.40	0.9	6.8			67/104	Findlay, Durham & Brodie

Date	Type of drum	Drum Dia. m	Drum width m	Drum cap. sq.m	Cyl. dia in.	Cyl. stroke in.	kW	Customer
1933	Double drum	4.30	1.5	20.3	40	72		Randfontein Gold Mines, SA
1933	Single drum	3.00	2.1	19.8	26	54		Victoria
1934	Double drum	3.70	1.2	13.9			947	City Deep, SA
1934	Double drum	3.00	0.9	8.5			280/546	Crown Mines, SA
1934	Conical drum	4.60	9.1	131.5			2005/4013	East Rand Mines, SA
1934	Conical drum	4.60	9.1	131.5			2005/4013	East Rand Mines, SA
1934	Conical drum	4.60	9.1	131.5			1787/3790	Durban Roodeport, SA
1934	Single drum	2.40	1.5	11.3			466	East Rand Mines, SA
1934	Double drum	3.40	2.5	26.7	30	60	295	Daggerfontein Mines, SA
1934	Double drum	3.40	2.5	26.7	25			Daggerfontein Mines, SA
1934	Double drum	3.40	2.5	26.7	40			
1934	Double drum	3.40	2.5	26.7	60			
1934	Conical drum	4.60	9.1	131.5			1787/3790	Durban Roodeport, SA
1934	Single drum	1.80	0.8	4.5			90/104	Glynnes Lydenburg, SA
1934	Single drum	4.30	1.7	23.0	33	72		Randfontein Gold Mines, SA
1934	Single drum	4.30	3.0	40.5			783/1529	Seaham
1934	Single drum	1.50	0.6	2.8		104	90/104	St John del Pay, Brazil
1934	Double drum	4.90	1.2	18.5			2984	Union Corporation, SA
1934	Double drum	4.90	1.2	18.5			2984	Union Corporation, SA
1934	Single drum	3.00	1.5	14.1	28	54		Witwatersrand Gold Mine, SA
1935	Double drum	2.10	1.1	7.3			345/496	Rose Deep
1935	Double drum	4.30	2.1	28.4			933	Comrie
1935	Single drum	3.00	3.7	34.9			448	Comrie
1935	Conical drum	4.00	6.1	76.7	30	72		Markham
1937	Single drum	4.30	1.7	23.0	36	72		Randfontein Gold Mines, SA
1938	Single drum	6.10	3.4	65.2	395		3954	Easington
1938	Single drum	6.10	3.4	65.2	395		3954	Easington
1938	Conical drum	4.30	7.9	106.7	36	72		Kilnhurst
1938	Single drum	4.30	2.4	32.4	30	60		Victoria
1939	Double drum	3.00	1.5	14.1			746	Rose Deep
1939	Double drum	3.00	1.5	14.1			261/627	Marfleet & Weight, Australia
1943	Single drum	4.00	2.2	27.6			834	Backworth
1943	Single drum	4.00	3.0	37.7			914	Backworth
1943	Single drum	3.40	1.9	20.3			578	Backworth
1945	Single drum	3.80	2.9	34.6			291	Arkwright
1945	Single drum						67/134	Backworth
1947	Double drum	6.10	1.7	32.6			1253/2506	Mansfield
1947	Single drum	6.10	3.2	61.3			2835/5670	Mansfield
1947	1-rope friction	8.20					2820	Rothes
1947	1-rope friction	8.20					2820	Rothes
1947	1-rope friction	8.20					2820	Rothes
1948	1-rope friction	7.30					883	Clipstone
1948	1-rope friction	7.30					2303/3305	Clipstone
1948	Single drum	3.00	1.2	11.3			336	Dalkeith
1949	Double drum	2.40	1.9	14.3			373/746	Marfleet & Weight, Australia
1952	2-rope friction	7.90					1865	Hem Heath
1952	Single drum	5.90	2.6	48.2			1865	Hem Heath
1953	Conical drum	4.40	7.3	100.9			1335/2456	Maltby Main
1953	4-rope friction	3.70					2225	Rufford
1953	4-rope friction	3.70					2550	Rufford
1954	4-rope friction	3.70					2947/5893	Maltby Main
1955	Single drum	4.30	3.0	40.5			1380/2200	New Hucknall
1955	Double drum	5.80	1.7	31.0			1753	Sutton
1955	Single drum	3.70	2.4	27.9			1044/2000	Teversal
1957	Double drum	3.00	1.2	11.3			821/1642	Marfleet & Weight, Australia
1957	Double drum	5.50	2.4	41.5			1119	Silverhill
1958	4-rope friction	3.70					2005	Bevercotes
1958	4-rope friction	3.70					2609	Bevercotes

Date	Type of drum	Drum Dia. m	Drum width m	Drum cap. sq.m	Cyl. dia in.	Cyl. stroke in.	kW	Customer
1958	4-rope friction	4.90					2387/4774	Wolstanton
1958	4-rope friction	4.90					2387/4774	Wolstanton
1959	4-rope friction	3.70					2014	Brodsworth
1959	4-rope friction	3.70					2014	Brodsworth
1959	Single drum	4.90	2.7	41.6			2710	Rufford
1960	Double drum	4.00	0.9	11.3			33	Newstead
1960	Single drum	6.10	3.4	65.2			1865	Shirebrook
1962	Single drum	6.10	4.0	76.7			1865	Daw Mill
1963	Single drum	5.40	3.7	62.8			2611/4633	Gresford - Dennis
1963	Single drum	4.90	4.0	61.6			1641	Gresford - Martin
1964	Single drum	4.90	2.6	40.0			1007	Horden
1964	Single drum	4.60	3.0	43.4			597	Hucknall
1964	4-rope friction	3.70					2 × 1074	Manton
1970	Single drum	2.60	1.8	14.7			746	Cape Breton, Canada
1974	Single drum	6.30	3.4	67.3			2611	Markham
1978	Double drum	3.80	1.4	16.7			933	Thyssen UK
1978	Single drum	6.10	2.5	47.9			2509	Brodsworth, British Coal
1978	Single drum	5.50	3.2	55.3			1119	Parsonage, BC
1978	Single drum	6.10	3.5	67.1			2163	Ollerton, BC
1978	Single drum	6.10	3.0	57.5			2126	Thorne, BC
1979	Single drum	6.10	3.0	57.5			2126	Thorne, BC
1979	2-rope friction	6.10					1294	Yorkshire Main, BC
1979	Single drum	6.10	2.7	51.7			2521	Markham Main, BC
1979	Single drum	7.30	3.0	68.8			2612	Bilsthorpe, BC
1980	Double drum	3.80	1.4	16.7			933	Thyssen UK
1980	Double drum	3.80	1.4	16.7			933	Thyssen UK
1980	Single drum	5.20	4.0	65.3			1590	Markham Main, BC
1980	Single drum	6.10	3.0	57.5			2238	Thoresby, BC
1981	6-rope friction	2.60					777	Selby Wistow, BC
1981	6-rope friction	2.60					777	Selby Riccall, BC
1981	6-rope friction	2.60					777	Selby Stillingfleet, BC
1982	Single drum	4.00	1.4	17.6			1119	Harmony Mine, Blaine & Co. Ltd
1982	Single drum	4.00	1.4	17.6			1119	Harmony Mine, Blaine & Co. Ltd
1983	Single drum	1.50	0.8	3.8			100	Doncaster HQ, BC
1983	Single drum mobile	1.50	0.8	3.8			100	Doncaster HQ, BC
1983	Single drum mobile	1.50	0.8	3.8			100	Doncaster HQ, BC
1983	Single drum mobile	1.50	0.8	3.8			100	Doncaster HQ, BC
1983	Single drum mobile	1.50	0.8	3.8			100	Doncaster HQ, BC
1985	6-rope friction	2.60					777	Selby Whitemoor, BC
1985	6-rope friction	2.60					777	North Selby, BC
1985	2-rope friction	7.30					2303	Clipstone, BC
1987	Ro-Ro winches							Kvaerner Cleveland Bridge
1987	Ro-Ro winches							Kvaerner Cleveland Bridge
1987	Ro-Ro winches							Kvaerner Cleveland Bridge
1987	Ro-Ro winches							Kvaerner Cleveland Bridge
1988	4-rope friction	4.00					1431	Asfordby, BC
1988	4-rope friction	4.00					1431	Asfordby, BC
1988	4-rope friction	3.40					720	Asfordby, BC
1988	4-rope friction	3.40					720	Asfordby, BC
1989	4-rope friction	5.20					3887	Harworth, BC
1989	3-rope friction	3.90					2626	Coleman Mine, INCO, Canada
1990	Double drum	3.60	1.2	13.6			970	Central No. 1 NEI, SGMC, Ghana
1990	Double drum	2.90	1.2	10.9			375	Central No. 2 NEI, SGMC, Ghana
1990	Double drum	2.90	1.2	10.9			375	AVS Man NEI, SGMC, Ghana

Date	Type of drum	Drum Dia. m	Drum width m	Drum cap. sq.m	Cyl. dia in.	Cyl. stroke in.	kW	Customer
1990	Double drum	2.90	1.2	10.9			375	AVS Rock NEI, SGMC, Ghana
1990	Double drum	2.90	1.2	10.9			260	Bondaye Main NEI, Ghana
1990	Double drum	2.90	1.2	10.9			375	AVS Decline NEI, Ghana
1990	Double drum	1.50	1.2	5.7			260	No. 6 shaft NEI, SGMC, Ghana
1990	Double drum	1.50	1.2	5.7			260	Fanti Rock NEI, SGMC, Ghana
1990	Single drum	1.50	1.2	5.7			150	Bondaye 16–14 NEI, SGMC, Ghana
1994	4-rope friction refurb	4.90					2387/4774	Harworth, BC
1994	Double drum	4.90	2.2	33.9			2665	Agnico Eagle, Canada
1994	Double drum refurb	6.10	2.6	49.8			2570	Placer Dome, Canada
1995	Single drum	4.57	2.5	35.9			2665	Agnico Eagle, Canada
1995	Double drum refurb	3.03	1.2	11.4			650	Cayeli Bakir, Turkey
1996	Double drum refurb	3.81	1.4	16.8			940	Stonewall Shaft, AGC, Ghana
1996	Double drum	3.66	2.1	24.1			2200	Placer Dome, Canada
1998	Single drum	2.56	1.4	10.9			450	Cayeli Bakir, Turkey
1999	2-single drums	0.58	0.6	1.1				Kvaerner Cementation, design only, Hong Kong
1999	Double drum	5.79	2.2	40.0			6000	Agnico Eagle, Canada

Date	Type of drum	Drum Dia. m	Drum width m	Drum cap. sq.m	Cyl. dia in.	Cyl. stroke in.	kW
Largest drum:							
1907	Yorkshire Main, conical	5.50	10.4		42	84	
Largest steam engines:							
1897	Grimethorpe	6.10	4.0		48	90	
1889	Shirebrook	7.40	3.6		48	90	
1904	Frickley	7.30	3.7		46	90	
Largest electric motor:							
1999	Agnico Eagle, Canada	5.79					6000

The total number of hoists was 297, of which 55 were for overseas.

Appendix 4: Specification of works plant capacity in the 1990s

Cranes:

Maximum lift by one crane   100 tonnes
Maximum lift by two cranes in tandem   150 tonnes
Maximum headroom under crane hook   12.8 m.

Fabrication equipment:

Burning gear   Semi automatic
Plate rolling   Vertical and horizontal
Welding plant   Manual metal arc
         Submerged arc
         MIG
         TIG
         Flux corded welding
         Manipulators to handle 80 tonnes
Stress relieving furnace: 7.2m. × 5.8m. × 3.3m. 50 tonnes maximum
Shot blasting facility

Machining capacity:

Lathes   up to 13m. between centres by 2m. swing, 65 tonnes max.
Vertical borers   8.1m. diameter × 4.2m. high
         5.36m. diameter × 3.265m. high
         11.9m. diameter × 4.94m. high

Ram type horizontal borers:

         9.5m. horizontal travel × 3.44m. vertical travel
         12.6m. horizontal travel × 5.33m. vertical travel
         12.0m. horizontal travel × 4.0m. vertical travel

NC table type borers:

         1.15m. × 2.0m. table × 1.6m. height
         1.0m. × 1.6m. table × 1.6m. height

Fitting & erection:

Erection pits and hydraulic test equipment

Site facilities:

Approved to BS 5750 part II with jacking and site machining plant

Quality assurance:

Approved to BS 5750 part II and BS 5882. Testing laboratory for NDT mechanical and weld testing.

Appendix 5: Financial results 1965–81

Year end	Sales	Pre-management charge profit	Profit	Shareholders' return on funds
	£'000	£'000	%	%
1965	8,020	1,366	17.0	14
1966	11,618	2,463	21.8	24
1967	11,274	2,721	24.1	20
1968	11,181	2,037	18.2	17
1969	11,929	1,545	13.0	13
1970	8,027	742	9.2	6
1971	9,352	553	6.0	5
1972	10,172	787	7.7	10
1973	16,897	1,763	10.4	20
1974	11,683	1,225	10.5	16
1975	10,273	910	8.9	15
1976	12,491	804	6.4	16
1977	11,742	1,118	9.5	18
1978	10,903	1,758	16.1	21
1979	18,782	4,105	21.9	60
1980	16,493	2,307	14.0	34
1981	14,180	1,745	12.3	30

Appendix 6: A summary of the NCB Rothes project, 1946–56

Plant etc.	Value at 1981 prices £
2 shaft sinking headgear	700,800
Internals for the winding towers	1,831,600
Mine car circulation equipment	1,465,280
Car hall, walkways and systems?	369,200
Underground on-setting gear	443,040
Overhead cranes	368,280
Cages and counterweights	461,500
Shaft furnishing for two shafts	784,550
Shaft inset steelwork	655,300
Rope changing winch and temporary winding gear	226,800
3 Koepe winders	1,563,000
Total	**£8,870,150**

Appendix 7: Contribution of water turbines to Markham order book 1977–92

Date	Water turbines £m.	Total orders £m.	% turbine orders
1977	0.4	4.2	9.5
1978	3.9	12.1	32.2
1979	0.9	3.4	26.5
1980	2.1	5.9	35.6
1981	4.0	5.8	69.0
1982	1.8	7.0	25.7
1983	6.4	12.8	50.0
1984	2.2	12.7	17.3
1985	1.7	11.9	14.3
1986	1.8	9.0	20.0
1987	2.6	4.8	54.2
1988	8.6	26.4	32.6
1989	0.8	9.2	8.7
1990	0.4	15.2	2.6
1991	8.2	20.9	39.2
1992	0.1	16.9	0.6
1993	8.8	16.3	54.0
Totals	**£54.7m.**	**£194.5m.**	**Av. 28.1%**